Skyline 2
▶▶ Video Activity Book

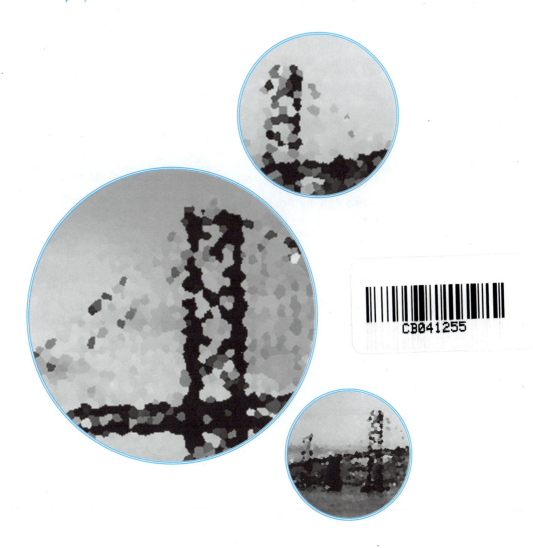

Martin McMorrow
Simon Brewster
Paul Davies
Mickey Rogers

How to use this Video Activity Book

Contents of the *Skyline* 2 Video

Our group of friends from the first *Skyline* video have moved on a year and are all now working in their first jobs. They are joined by Mariana, a creative writer from Venezuela and Jin, a biology major from Hong Kong. We follow the group through a year as their lives and situations change against the backdrop of life in Boston. Josh finds romance at last, but what about Jennifer? And will Shawna get her promotion at the ad agency? They all work hard, have fun and get along well … most of the time!

The language that students are exposed to is natural, everyday, contemporary American English. While the language is above the students' productive capabilities, the tasks have been carefully chosen to focus their attention and minimize the difficulty of comprehension.

The themes, vocabulary and language focus of each unit in the *Skyline* 2 Video tie in closely with the corresponding unit in *Skyline* 2 Student's Book. Therefore, students who use this coursebook will not have to learn new grammatical structures or vocabulary.

Structure of the *Skyline* 2 Video and the Video Activity Book

The *Skyline* 2 Video Course consists of 12 units. Each unit is approximately four or five minutes long and is divided into a number of shorter scenes, which are lettered A, B, C, etc. The Video Activity Book mirrors the video and consists of photocopiable *Student's worksheets* and the *Teacher's notes* accompanying them. The lessons are divided into five main sections: *Before you watch*; *Watch for main ideas*; *Watch for details*; *After you watch*, and *Communication activity*.

Worksheets

1 Before you watch

This section consists of a cultural note and exercises. The cultural note provides relevant information about one of the themes in the unit. The students perform one or more tasks chosen to stimulate their interest in and knowledge of the chosen theme. Examples of the tasks and activities are:
- vocabulary exercises to pre-teach certain key items.
- discussion / information-sharing on the theme of the unit.
- ranking of statements / items according to specific criteria / personal values.
- brainstorming exercises.
- prediction exercises based on a variety of cues including photographs, drawings, etc.

2 Watch for main ideas

The first viewing activity is called *Watch for main ideas*. The students focus their attention on the major story highlights. Typical tasks include:
- matching activities focusing on general comprehension.
- ordering activities with visuals or limited reading.
- marking boxes or sentences with checks (✔), which is quicker than writing and allows the students to concentrate more on the visual stimuli.
- basic note taking / gap filling.
- completing or labeling a diagram.

3 Watch for details

During the second viewing, each scene is looked at again but this time in more detail. Usually, the students look at the task and carry it out first before watching the scene again to check their answers. This ensures that they are familiar with the task and requires them to spend less time reading while they are watching. However, it is important that your students understand that they are not expected to get all the answers right before they watch the scene again. Compared to the *Watch for main ideas* tasks, the *Watch for details* tasks usually involve more of a linguistic focus and / or more reading or extensive note taking.

4 After you watch

The *After you watch* section consists of grammatical, lexical or functional activities. There is also some skills development work with a particular focus on speaking and / or writing. *After you watch* tasks include:
- text completion.
- working with summaries of events in the unit.
- various writing tasks such as narrative accounts of events in the unit.
- giving personal reactions to ideas / events in the unit.
- role-play and simulation.

Teacher's notes

The detailed *Teacher's notes* contain:
- a scene-by-scene summary of each unit.
- detailed instructions on how to use the course.
- suggestions on ways to pre-teach new language.
- the answer key.
- useful practical reminders, such as when to rewind the tape!
- links to the *Communication activities* at the back of the book.
- the entire video script with scene changes.

In addition to the four sections in the *Teacher's notes*, there is a fifth section.

5 Communication activity

This feature only appears in the *Teacher's notes* so that you can decide whether to use the activity in a lesson or not. Each unit finishes with a communication activity that provides additional practice of each unit's topic and language work. The tasks are all based on an information-gap or opinion-gap principle and are designed to promote speaking and listening skills in a freer, more relaxed context.

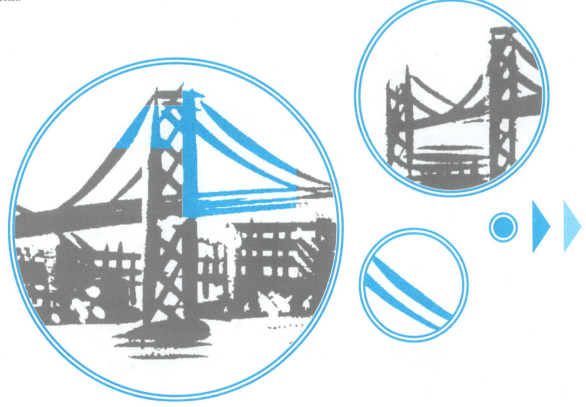

Contents

Unit			Summary	Cultural note	Language	Vocabulary	Communication activities
1	Welcome to Boston 00:00 – 05:28	8	Mariana arrives in Boston, is picked up by Luis and meets her new roommates and neighbors.	The city of Boston	● Meeting people	● Travel	Saying it without words – a mime game
2	A new job 05:35 – 11:45	12	Mariana meets her new boss and finds out about the company. At home, she meets Jin and they talk about their countries and the U.S.	The Hispanic population of the United States	● *much / many / a lot of*	● Business ● Office equipment	Designing your new office – a pairwork activity
3	Matchmaker 11:51 – 16:58	16	Joan introduces the Fruity Fruit project. Shawna shows Cal how to buy a car on the Internet and they go to a movie. Jennifer talks about her video from the dating agency.	The Internet	● *be / have* with descriptions	● Advertising ● Looks ● Cars	What's the best way of …? – a discussion
4	Cleaning up 17:05 – 22:41	20	Both the boys' and the girls' apartments are a mess. There's an argument in each apartment about who's responsible, but both apartments get cleaned.	No Housework Day	● Gerunds after verbs of liking / disliking	● Housework	Spot the differences – a communication gap activity
5	Dream date 22:47 – 29:47	24	Mariana's lonely so Jennifer encourages her to choose a man from the dating video. She didn't enjoy the date but the next day she begins to see Josh in a new light.	Dating services	● Future with *going to*	● Dating ● Adjectives for feelings	Dating agency – a communication gap and discussion activity
6	A bad day 29:53 – 35:22	28	Just as the friends finish their work, the system goes down. They have to work until very late. Cal brings them food but later forgets where his car is and thinks it was stolen.	Overwork	● Past simple and progressive	● Work expressions	Computer trouble – a jigsaw story
7	Play-off game 36:50 – 40:56	32	The friends are watching a game of American football on TV. Jin can't work with the noise, so Mariana lets him study in her apartment.	American football	● Comparatives	● American football ● Adjectives about sport	Find someone who … – a communication gap activity

Unit			Summary	Cultural note	Language	Vocabulary	Communication activities
8	**Presidents' Day weekend** 41:01 – 45:10	36	The friends decide to go skiing for the holiday weekend. Josh wants to go but has to persuade his sister to let him go, because he's supposed to go on a family visit.	National holidays	• *too* and *either*	• Skiing • Adjectives about sport	Agreement – a conversation game
9	**Pain in the neck** 45:16 – 49:25	40	The friends are in the ski lodge. We learn about Shiatsu massage and Jin recommends Josh has one for his shoulder injury. He is sceptical but tries it out and it's a great success.	Alternative therapy	• *should / need to / have to*	• Sickness and therapy	Rules and advice – a team game
10	**Getting stood up** 49:31 – 56:31	44	Josh phones Mariana to check she's going to Cal's party, but she doesn't arrive there so he gets depressed. She arrives after he's left and phones him to explain that in Venezuela it's normal to go to parties later.	Parties	• Present perfect	• Dating • Party and barbecue food	The party game – a role-play
11	**A promotion** 56:37 – 61:30	48	Joan announces that they've won the Fruity Fruit account. Shawna complains to Al about her work and he encourages her to ask Joan for a raise. But Joan says it's not possible now, so Shawna says she may leave.	Discrimination at work	• *do* and *make*	• Tasks at work	Asking for a raise – a role-play
12	**Predicting the future** 61:39 – 67:52	52	The friends go to Jennifer's store where Jin reads their horoscopes. Joan gives Shawna a raise.	Astrology	• Future forms • Connectors	• Character adjectives • Animals	*Skyline* video quiz – an end-of-course quiz

Communication activities	56
Review Unit for Units 1–6	64

v

▶▶ Meet the characters

Many of the characters in the *Skyline* 2 Video Activity Book will be familiar to students and teachers who have used Book 1. The main new characters in Book 2 are Mariana and Jin. Mariana, Shawna and Sara share an apartment together and Jin shares the next-door apartment with Luis and Josh. In this video there is more of a focus on the workplace. Mariana, Luis and Shawna all work for the advertising agency McDonald Portman. Two other characters, Joan Portman and Al, work at the agency. The couples from Book 1, Shawna and Cal, and Luis and Sara, are still together. During Book 2, the growing love-interest is between Mariana and Josh.

▶▶ Mariana

Mariana comes to Boston from her hometown of Caracas in Venezuela to work for an advertising agency called McDonald Portman. She is a copywriter, which means that she writes the material for advertisements, and the company has employed her because they want to expand in the Hispanic market. Shawna and Luis work for the same company and it is Luis who picks her up from the airport. They work hard together to win an important new account and after some problems they are successful. Mariana is cheerful but sensitive and has some difficulties getting used to life in the United States. She also feels a bit lonely and tries meeting a guy she sees on a video from a dating agency. This is a disaster. She starts off by looking down on Josh, but as she finds out more about him, she becomes increasingly attracted to him – as he does to her!

▶▶ Josh

Josh was born and grew up in Boston. He shares an apartment with Luis and Jin. He's a social work student, but he's crazy about sports, his other interests being drinking beer, eating burgers and watching TV. He's fun to be around. In Video 1, he encourages Luis to pursue Sara, without realizing that his sister, Jennifer, is interested in Luis. In Video 2, Josh becomes interested in Mariana, but she finds him a bit superficial. However, as she later discovers, he has a sensitive and caring side to him. He wants to be a social worker and helps kids play basketball in his spare time. He notices Mariana is getting keener on him and he misses a family get-together to go skiing with her and the other friends. He's very hurt when he doesn't see her at Cal's barbecue but forgives her quickly when he realizes it's all been a misunderstanding.

▶▶ Shawna

Shawna is from Chicago, where her dad is a police officer and her mother a nurse. In Video 1 Shawna is studying business and art history. She meets Cal at a cookout and falls for him. In Video 2 Shawna is now an office manager at the advertising agency McDonald Portman. She is hard-working and cheerful. She has a lot of different responsibilities and shows Mariana around the office when she arrives. She begins to feel that she isn't really appreciated and asks Joan for a raise. She worries that she's done the wrong thing, but it works out positively in the end. She's still dating Cal and she makes sure she gets what she wants – like going to see a romantic movie together, even when he's not really interested!

▶▶ Cal

Cal grew up in New York City and his father was a car mechanic before he died. Cal also loves cars. In Video 1 Cal is studying engineering. He meets Shawna at a cookout and immediately falls for her. In Video 2 their relationship has developed. He now has a job and wants to get a new car that suits his new status. Shawna shows him how to get information about it on the Internet. Cal is kind and helpful. When Shawna has to cancel their date in order to work late with Luis and Mariana, he goes and gets them all food. However, he forgets where he parks and thinks his new car's been stolen! He's sociable and invites the friends over to his place for a barbecue – where Josh gets depressed because Mariana hasn't arrived.

▶▶ Jennifer

Jennifer (or "Jen") is Josh's sister. She was born in Boston and grew up there, too. She is single and, in Video 1, is very attracted to Luis, but he starts to date Sara. In Video 2, Jennifer still has her store selling books, candles, oils, music, and so on, and all her friends visit her there in order to try to predict the future. Jennifer is still single and without a boyfriend in Video 2, and she has joined a video dating agency. She notices that Mariana is lonely and persuades her to try it – it isn't a success!

▶▶ Jin

Jin is a biology student from Hong Kong. He's been in the United States for four years already. He is a serious student and sometimes gets annoyed with the untidiness and noise of his roommates. He is sympathetic to people with problems: he reassures Mariana soon after she arrives, offers ginger tea and sympathy to Josh at the barbecue and is very positive about Shawna's prospects of promotion when he reads the Chinese horoscopes of all of his friends.

▶▶ Luis

Luis is Brazilian. His father is Brazilian and his mother is American. In Video 1 Luis comes to Boston to study graphic design. He meets Josh and Jennifer, and he meets and becomes involved with Sara. In Video 2 Luis is working as a graphic designer for an advertising agency. He picks up Mariana from the airport and tells her a bit about Boston on the way back to her apartment. He's quiet and serious. His relationship with Sara is becoming more serious in Video 2.

▶▶ Sara

Sara grew up in Vancouver and has a Canadian mother and an American father. She loves music and plays in a band. In Video 1, she meets and falls for Luis, and they become very close. In Video 2, their relationship continues to grow. Sara now shares an apartment with Shawna and Mariana, but she's not very tidy and this causes a bit of tension. But she does help everyone tidy up and agrees to do her fair share in future.

▶▶ Joan

Joan is totally focused on her work – running her own advertising company – and she expects the same dedication from her employees. She doesn't waste time chatting – everything she says is about what has to be done. When there's a danger that they won't finish the presentation for the new account because there have been computer problems, she insists that everyone stays late until they've finished the project. She gives very little praise and this leaves Shawna feeling unappreciated. However, Joan is clever enough to realize that Shawna is too good to lose and she does offer a raise – with one condition: it must be earned.

▶▶ Al

Al is responsible for the computer systems at McDonald Portman. He explains to Mariana how to use the network on her first day and promises to solve the serious problem when the server goes down just as Mariana, Luis and Shawna are finishing their work on the Fruity Fruit presentation. He comes across as cool and a bit arrogant, but shows a more sensitive and caring side when he sympathizes with Shawna and encourages her to ask for a raise.

Unit One 1   Teacher's notes

Welcome to Boston – Summary

In scene 1A, we receive a brief tourist introduction to Boston and see some of the main sights and images of the city. In scene 1B, Mariana arrives at the airport and fills out her I-94 form. She is met by Luis and he shows her some of the sights of Boston as he drives her to her new apartment. In scene 1C, she is introduced to her new roommates, Shawna and Sara, and discovers that Sara is also from a different country. She also meets Luis's roommate, Josh. All of these characters may be familiar from *Skyline* Video 1.

1 Before you watch

▶▶ **Cultural note**

a ● Use the picture on page 12 of the Student's Book to introduce the situation. If any of the students have traveled to the United States, have them tell the others about arriving there.
  ● Ask the students to read the cultural note.
b ● Pre-teach any new vocabulary as necessary, e.g. *roommate* (a person living in the same apartment as another), *sights* (places of interest).
  ● Have the students do the exercise in pairs.
  ● Check their answers.

> **Answers:** 1c 2e 3d 4a 5b

c ● Have the students share their ideas in pairs and then write the best ideas on the board.

2 Watch for main ideas   `00:00 – 05:28`

  ● Have the students predict the order of the events. Ask them: *What happens when you arrive in a new country?*
  ● Get them to compare their ideas with the ones on the list and predict the order.
  ● Play the video for them to check their answers.

> **Answers:** 5a 6b 3c 7d 1e 2f 4g

◀◀ Rewind the video to 1A 00:23 in preparation for **Watch for details**.

3 Watch for details   `scene 1A: 00:23 – 01:03`

a ● Check the list to ensure that the students know the vocabulary.
  ● Have the students watch the video and check (✔) the things they see.
  ● Check their answers.

> **Answers:** an aquarium, a park, an outdoor concert, a historic monument, people wearing traditional costume

b ● Have the students discuss the follow-up questions in pairs. If necessary, help them by asking: *Does your town / city have an aquarium / a park?* etc.

▶▶ **Scene 1B: 01:05 – 03:47**

  ● Have the students watch the video and mark the statements true or false.
  ● You could ask them to correct the false statements.
  ● Check their answers.

> **Answers:** 1F (She comes from Venezuela.) 2F (She filled out her I-94 form at the airport.) 3T 4F (It was easy.) 5T 6T 7F (Luis drives her.) 8F (The river is called the Charles River.)

▶▶ **Scene 1C: 03:50 – 05:28**

a ● Have the students watch the video and match up the names and photographs.
  ● Check their answers.

> **Answers:** 1E 2B 3A 4C 5D

b ● Ask the students to try to complete the table.
  ● Tell them they can compare in pairs.
  ● If you wish, rewind and play the scene again for them to check.
  ● Check their answers.

> **Answers:**
>
> | Mariana | Luis | Sara | Shawna | Josh | |
> |---------|------|------|--------|------|--|
> | ✔ | ✔ | | ✔ | | are going to work together. |
> | ✔ | ✔ | ✔ | | | came to Boston from another country. |
> | ✔ | ✔ | ✔ | ✔ | ✔ | are going to live in the same building. |
> | | | | ✔ | ✔ | are going to play basketball. |

4 After you watch

Language focus: meeting people

a ● Have the students do the exercise in pairs.
  ● Check their answers, helping with pronunciation as necessary.

> **Answers:** 1 in → to 2 come → coming 3 she → this 4 I → to 5 excited → exciting 6 doing → going

b ● Have the students prepare what they are going to say before the role-play. Ask them what people normally say when they meet for the first time in an airport or train station, e.g. *Did you have a good trip / flight?*
  ● Then ask the students what other things they might ask, e.g. *Are you tired? Would you like a cup of coffee? Do you know Boston / the U.S.A.?* etc.
  ● Have a strong pair demonstrate the role-play in front of the class.
  ● Then ask the students to practice in pairs. Move around the class, listening and noting errors, which can be corrected at the end of the activity.

5 Communication activity

Turn to page 56 for the *Saying it without words* activity.

Video Script

COUNTER 00:00–05:28

Scene 1A: 00:23 – 01:03

Announcer: Boston's a city of spectacular heights, and mysterious depths. It's big splashes, and small ponds. It's lazy walks in the park, and runs by the river. It's conductors … and conductors. It's a man with a vision, and a field of dreams. It's old times, and new. It's an explosion of history and quiet moments in which to reflect. And it's birds, of all kinds.

Scene 1B: 01:05 – 03:47

Official: Good morning, and welcome to the United States. Is this your final destination?

Mariana: Yes, Boston.

Official: Do you have your I-94 form?

Mariana: My I-94 form? Oh, yes! Oh no, but I forgot to fill it out.

Official: That's OK. You can fill it out at that table right back there.

Mariana: OK. Thank you. Oh, this looks so hard, let me see. OK, complete both arrival record items one through 13 and departure record items 14 through 17. OK, I can do this. Item 1, family name, Romero, item 2, first name, Mariana. This isn't that hard. Hmm. Birthdate, date 18, month 8, year 1977. Finally, item 17, Venezuela, I did it! That was easy.

Mariana: Hello, Luis?

Luis: Yes, Mariana.

Mariana: Hi, so good to meet you. Thank you so much for coming to pick me up.

Luis: Oh, that's no problem. Welcome to Boston.

Mariana: Thank you.

Luis: How was your flight?

Mariana: Oh. It was long. I'm pretty tired, but I'm really happy to be here!

Luis: I'm right out here.

Mariana: What's going on over here?

Luis: This er, city's under construction right now, OK, OK and that's Boston, …

Mariana: Oh …

Luis: Right over there, the big city.

Mariana: And what are they building in there?

Luis: Er, they're remodeling the airport right now actually.

Mariana: Is that the Charles River?

Luis: Yes, right. Er … they have concerts over there … and, er, that's MIT right across the river.

Mariana: What's MIT?

Luis: Oh, the Massachusetts Institute of Technology … and er, Harvard's right up there too.

Scene 1C: 03:50 – 05:28

Luis: Hey Sara, er, this is Mariana. Mariana, Sara.

Sara: Hi, Mariana. It's nice to meet you.

Mariana: Hi, Sara. It's nice to meet you, too.

Luis: Oh, this is Shawna.

Shawna: Hi, Mariana. Good to meet you. Welcome to Boston.

Mariana: Oh, thank you, Shawna. It's so exciting to be here. To have a job here and …

Shawna: You know, Mariana, you and I will be working together. I'm the new office manager at the ad agency. Luis helped me get the job.

Mariana: Oh, that's great!

Shawna: So where are you from?

Mariana: I'm from Caracas, in Venezuela.

Shawna: Oh, wow.

Sara: Venezuela must be beautiful.

Mariana: It is very beautiful. And where are you from?

Sara: I'm from Vancouver, British Columbia. In Canada.

Shawna: And I'm from Chicago, Illinois.

Luis: São Paulo, Brazil.

Josh: Hey, how's it going? Hey, there. I'm Josh!

Mariana: Hi. I'm Mariana.

Josh: Nice to meet you.

Mariana: Nice to meet you, too.

Luis: Josh is my roommate. We live in the building.

Josh: Yeah, so you'll be seeing me all the time!

Mariana: Oh, I see.

Josh: Shawna, you wanna go shoot some hoops? I'm going down to the park.

Shawna: Sure, sounds good. Let's go.

Mariana: Shoot some hoops?

Luis: Yeah, shoot some hoops. It means "play basketball."

Mariana: Oh.

Sara: He's a really nice guy.

Mariana: Oh. Welcome to the United States … Welcome to Boston … Welcome to the United States … You wanna go shoot some hoops? … You wanna go shoot some hoops? … Welcome to Boston … Nice to meet you … Nice to meet you … so you'll be seeing me all the time …

Unit One **1**

Welcome to Boston

1 Before you watch

▶▶ **Cultural note**

a Read the text.

Boston, Massachusetts, is the largest city in New England, on the northeast coast of the United States. It is a historic city with modern industries and businesses and is a major cultural and educational center, with two of America's most famous universities – Harvard and MIT (the Massachusetts Institute of Technology).

b In this unit, Mariana arrives in Boston. Here are some of the things that happen to her. Match the beginnings of the sentences with the endings.

1 She goes through	a some of Boston's sights.
2 She fills out	b her new roommates.
3 A colleague picks her up	c immigration.
4 He points out	d in the arrivals area.
5 He introduces her to	e a form for visitors to the U.S.

c What are the good and bad things about traveling to another country? Make a note of two good things and two bad things, then compare your ideas with a partner.

2 Watch for main ideas

a You're going to watch part of Mariana's first day in Boston. What do you think is the correct order of these events? Write a to g.

1 She sees some of Boston's sights.		5 She arrives in the United States.	a
2 She meets her new roommates.		6 She talks to an immigration official.	
3 She fills out an immigration form.		7 Her colleague picks her up.	
4 She has a dream about her day.			

b Watch the video and check your answers.

3 Watch for details

▶▶ **Scene 1A**

a Check (✔) the things you see on the video.

an aquarium	☑	a park	☐	an outdoor concert	☐
a historic monument	☐	a football game	☐	people wearing traditional costume	☐
an art gallery	☐				

b Does Boston look different from your town / city? Would you like to live there?

▶▶ **Scene 1B**

Watch the video and mark the statements T (True) or F (False).

1 Mariana comes from Colombia.	T	☐	F	☐
2 Mariana filled out her I-94 form on the plane.	T	☐	F	☐
3 There are 17 items on the form.	T	☐	F	☐
4 It's hard to fill out the form.	T	☐	F	☐
5 Mariana had a long flight.	T	☐	F	☐
6 There's a lot of construction work in Boston.	T	☐	F	☐
7 They take a taxi from the airport.	T	☐	F	☐
8 The river in Boston is called the Hudson.	T	☐	F	☐

PHOTOCOPIABLE

Copyright © Macmillan Publishers Limited 2002.

Worksheet
Welcome to Boston

▶▶ Scene 1C

a Watch scene 1C and match the names with the photographs.

1 Josh   2 Luis   3 Mariana   4 Sara   5 Shawna

b Check (✔) the correct box or boxes for each sentence.

Mariana	Luis	Sara	Shawna	Josh	
					are going to work together.
					came to Boston from another country.
					are going to live in the same building.
					are going to play basketball.

4 After you watch

Language focus: meeting people

a Correct the mistake in each line.

1 **Official:** Good morning, and welcome in the United States.
2 **Mariana:** Thank you so much for come to pick me up.
3 **Luis:** Hey Sara, she is Mariana. Mariana, Sara.
4 **Sara:** Hi, Mariana. It's nice I meet you.
5 **Mariana:** Oh, thank you, Shawna. It's so excited to be here.
6 **Josh:** Hey, how's it doing?

b Use these notes to have a conversation like Luis and Mariana. Student A is arriving at the airport. Student B is your colleague, but has never seen you before.

Student A

- Introduce yourself to your colleague.
- Talk about your flight and thank your colleague for meeting you.
- Refuse politely.
- Refuse politely.
- Thank your colleague again.

Student B

- Introduce yourself and ask about the flight.
- Offer to take your colleague's bags.
- Offer to buy your colleague a cup of coffee.
- Show your colleague the way to your car.

Unit Two 2

Teacher's notes

A new job — Summary

In scene 2A, we learn about the advertising agency, McDonald Portman. Mariana meets her boss, Joan, who looks as though she will be a really horrible boss. Mariana is then shown around the office by Shawna. In scene 2B, Al helps Mariana with the computer system. In scene 2C, Joan shows Mariana some of the market research about beverages and Luis shows her some of his work. In scene 2D, Mariana is back in her apartment, where she meets Jin, a biology student who lives across the hall with Josh and Luis. Jin comes from Hong Kong, and he and Mariana talk about how different America is from their countries.

1 Before you watch

▶▶ **Cultural note**
- Read the cultural note with the students and see if any of them are surprised by it.
- Use the discussion questions to raise the issue of minority communities in a country.
- Discuss how the integration of ethnic minorities can affect a country, in both good and bad ways, e.g. *bringing variety, helping people to understand others*.

2 Watch for main ideas 05:35 – 11:45

- Pre-teach any new vocabulary as necessary, e.g. *ad* (short form of *advertisement*), *trend* (a general tendency or direction), *research* (study to find new facts or information), *beverage* (any type of drink except water).
- Have the students look at the three people in the photographs.
- Ask them to try to match the people with the labels, working in pairs or groups.
- Play the video for the students to check their answers before you check as a class.

Answers: Joan: unfriendly, Mariana's new boss; Al: helpful, responsible for IT in the company; Jin: serious, a biology student

◀◀ Rewind the video to 2A 05:51 in preparation for **Watch for details**.

3 Watch for details Scene 2A: 05:51 – 07:31

a • Have the students write the names of the items next to the pictures. They can look at page 14 of the Student's Book or in a dictionary for help.
  • Either check their answers around the class or play scene 2A once for the students to check themselves.
b • Have the students watch the scene again and number the pictures as they see them in the video.
  • Check their answers.

Answers: A kitchen (6), B conference room (5), C stationery (2), D photocopier (1), E printer (4), F fax machine (3), G restroom (7)

▶▶ **Scene 2B: 07:34 – 08:18**

- Have the students read the sentences and try to cross out the extra words.
- Play the scene for them to check their answers before you check as a class.

Answers: 1 to 2 in 3 for 4 to 5 to

▶▶ **Scene 2C: 08:21 – 09:18**

- Have the students predict the answers and mark the statements true or false.
- Play the scene for them to check their answers.
- After the students have checked their answers, have them correct the statements that are false.

Answers: 1T 2F (She shows them the research on national trends.) 3F (She asks her to read about their current research.) 4T 5F (She receives a call, but loses it.)

▶▶ **Scene 2D: 09:21 – 11:45**

- Have the students check (✔) the correct column as they watch the scene.
- Check their answers.

Answers: 2 Jin 3 Mariana 4 Mariana and Jin 5 Jin 6 Mariana

4 After you watch

Language focus: *much, many, a lot (of)*
- Have the students check the grammar on page 17 of their Student's Books.
- **Note:** *of* is only used with *a lot* when followed by a noun or pronoun. Although Jin says: *There are **many** differences*, it's more common to use *a lot of* in affirmative sentences.
- Have the students complete the sentences. Check answers around the class.

Answers: 1 a lot of 2 many 3 much 4 a lot of 5 a lot 6 many 7 much 8 a lot of 9 a lot 10 much

Discussion
- Have the students do this in pairs or groups of three or four.
- If necessary, help the students by asking a few questions, e.g., *What kind of food do you / Americans eat? Does every family here / in the U.S. have a car?* etc.
- Note, but don't correct errors with comparatives – this is covered in Unit 7.

5 Communication activity

Turn to page 56 for the *Designing your new office* activity.

Video Script

Scene 2A: 05:51 – 07:31

Announcer: McDonald Portman … a full service advertising agency …with the top writers and artists … complete market research … and a global presence, with offices around the world. McDonald Portman, helping your message go global.

Joan: So, Mariana, you're the writer from the agency in Venezuela?

Mariana: Yes, that's right. I'm from Caracas.

Joan: Oh, I'm glad you're here. I'm Joan Portman. And we really need someone that writes well in Spanish.

Mariana: Thanks a lot.

Joan: Oh, I'm sure you're going to be able to help us with all the Hispanic accounts.

Mariana: Oh, yes, of course.

Joan: OK, well this is Shawna and she's going to show you around the office today. Welcome to McDonald Portman.

Mariana: Thanks.

Shawna: Let's start our tour at the front of the building. The photocopier's here.

Mariana: And where's the paper?

Shawna: Oh, the extra paper is up here … and the stationery is down here … the fax machine is right here … and the printer's over there. That's Joan's office right there …

Mariana: And what's in there?

Shawna: Oh, that's a conference room. Here's the kitchen. We usually have lunch in here. There's always coffee over there … and tea.

Mariana: Uh, Shawna. Where is the restroom?

Shawna: Oh, the restroom is right here. And here's Al. Al, this is Mariana, she's our new writer from Venezuela.

Al: Hi, Mariana.

Mariana: Hi, Al. Nice to meet you.

Shawna: She needs to get set up on the email and everything.

Al: Email, sure. No problem. Oh, I mean no problema. No problema.

Mariana: Thanks a lot.

Scene 2B: 07:34 – 08:18

Al: OK, this is your computer.

Mariana: Great.

Al: Let's start with your password. And open your email account. I set it up for you yesterday.

Mariana: Thanks a lot.

Al: Sure. OK, now we're ready. Enter the password you want.

Mariana: OK. Here's my password.

Al: Good. That's it. You are ready to go.

Mariana: Thanks, Al. Oh, and how do I get into the server?

Al: Just click here and … click on this icon … and there you go. You are in the server.

Mariana: Hmm, thanks, OK, I think I'm all set for now. Thanks a lot, Al.

Al: Hey, it's my job. Call me if you have any problems. OK?

Mariana: I'll see you later.

Al: Bye.

Scene 2C: 08:21 – 09:18

Joan: As you know, we do a lot of work in beverages … juices … sports drinks … It's a huge market, but very competitive. Very competitive. Here's our research. Research on national trends – who's buying what – how old they are – how much money they spend – the flavors they like – the colors they like … So please read this information about what we're doing.

Luis: Here are some graphic ideas I'm working on. Let me show you …

Mariana: Oh, nice colors.

Luis: Thanks.

Shawna: Mariana, call for you.

Mariana: Er, what do I do?

Shawna: Press the flashing green light on the phone.

Mariana: Yes. Oh, I see. Hello? Hello? Oh no …

Scene 2D: 09:21 – 11:45

Jin: Hey, is Luis or Josh here?

Mariana: No.

Jin: Uh, I'm sorry. I'm Jin. Luis and Josh's roommate.

Mariana: Oh, hi. I'm Mariana. I'm Sara and Shawna's roommate. Er … so … what do you do?

Jin: I'm a student. I study biology. I hope to go to medical school next year.

Mariana: Oh … so you're going to be a doctor?

Jin: Er, I hope so!

Mariana: Uh … So how long have you been here?

Jin: I've been here about four years.

Mariana: Four years! Wow, that's a long time. I just got here yesterday.

Jin: What about you? What are you doing here?

Mariana: I'm a writer. I work at an ad agency with Luis and Shawna.

Jin: Ah, you look pretty tired.

Mariana: Oh, I am tired. It's been a long day!

Jin: I know. Everything is so different. It makes it hard at first.

Mariana: Yeah. So many things are different … like lunch. In Caracas, we have two hours for lunch. It's a big meal of the day. Here, the lunch breaks are so short! People don't eat much … maybe like, er, a salad … or a sandwich … or a slice of pizza.

Jin: In Hong Kong, they take a longer lunch, too.

Mariana: So are there many other differences from Hong Kong?

Jin: There are many differences. Here, the streets are much less crowded. In Hong Kong, there are people everywhere. The streets are full of vendors – selling everything you can imagine. From chickens to snakes … What about you? What are the differences for you?

Mariana: Oh, well, for me the biggest difference right now is speaking English all day! I'm so tired!

Jin: Yeah, I know, speaking English all day is very hard, especially at first. But your English is excellent.

Mariana: Oh, thanks a lot.

Josh: Hey, you guys. Jin! How's it going?

Jin: Hey Josh. I'm fine.

Josh: You guys want some pizza?

Jin: Pizza? OK. Sounds good.

Josh: How about you, Mariana? Want some pizza? Come on.

Mariana: No …

Josh: It's still hot!

Mariana: I …

Jin: Come on, let's have some.

Mariana: OK. Why not? It's just that I had pizza for lunch, too!

13

Unit Two 2

A new job

1 Before you watch

▶▶ **Cultural note**

Read the text and then discuss the questions.

The Hispanic population of the United States is large and growing. Already one in ten of all Americans consider themselves to be Hispanic and in some areas, like southern California, they are now the largest ethnic group. Companies need to consider this at every stage of the design and promotion of their products and services.

1 Does your country have a lot of people from another area / background? Who are they?
2 How does this affect your country?

2 Watch for main ideas

a Try to match the descriptions with the photographs of people from this unit.

 Joan  Al  Jin

| helpful | serious | unfriendly | a biology student | Mariana's new boss | responsible for IT in the company |

b Now watch the video and check your answers.

3 Watch for details

▶▶ **Scene 2A**

a Write the names of the things and places in an office under the pictures.

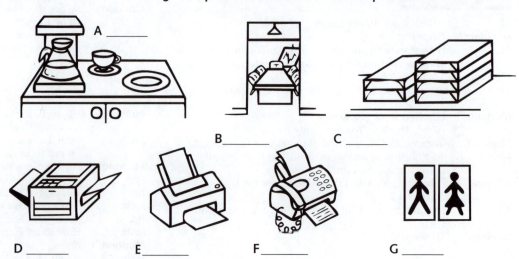

A _____   B _____   C _____   D _____   E _____   F _____   G _____

b Watch scene 2A and number the pictures in the order you see them in the video.

Worksheet
A new job

▶▶ Scene 2B

a **Cross out an extra word in each of Al's sentences. Look at the example.**

This is ~~the~~ your computer.
1 Let's to start with your password.
2 Enter in the password you want.
3 You are ready for to go.
4 Click on to this icon and there you go.
5 Call to me if you have any problems.

b Now watch scene 2B and check your answers.

▶▶ Scene 2C

a **Read statements 1–5. Mark each one T (True) or F (False).**

1 Drinks are an important part of the company's work.   T ☐   F ☐
2 Joan shows them research on global trends.   T ☐   F ☐
3 She asks Mariana to read about their future plans.   T ☐   F ☐
4 Luis shows Mariana some of his artwork.   T ☐   F ☐
5 Mariana makes a telephone call.   T ☐   F ☐

b Now watch scene 2C and check your answers.

▶▶ Scene 2D

Watch the video. Check (✔) the person who goes with each sentence.

	Mariana	Jin	
1	✔		works at an ad agency.
2			arrived in Boston four years ago.
3			is very tired.
4			has a long lunch in his / her own country.
5			comes from a crowded city.
6			had pizza for lunch.

4 After you watch

Language focus: *much, many, a lot (of)*
Complete these sentences with *much, many, a lot* **or** *a lot of*.

1 Shawna gives Mariana _____ information about the office.
2 The agency doesn't have _____ Spanish speakers in Boston.
3 There isn't _____ space to have lunch in the office.
4 The agency does _____ work with beverages.
5 Al knows _____ about computers.
6 Mariana doesn't have _____ problems on her first day.
7 Americans don't spend _____ time having lunch.
8 There are always _____ vendors on the streets in Hong Kong.
9 Mariana says, "Thanks _____ " to Shawna, Al and Jin.
10 Mariana doesn't see _____ variety in American food.

Discussion

Would you like to study in America (like Jin) or work there (like Mariana)?
Use these ideas to talk about the differences you would find there.

| food | cars | clothes | how the people look |
| work | houses | sports | family life |

Unit Three 3

Teacher's notes

Matchmaker – Summary

A matchmaker is a person who introduces two others in the hope that a romantic relationship will be the result. It can be used more generally to refer to bringing people or things together, and in this unit could refer to Cal and his car or Jennifer and a man. In scene 3A, Joan introduces the Fruity Fruit drinks campaign to Luis, Mariana and Shawna. She gets impatient with Mariana's questions. In scene 3B, Shawna and Cal plan their evening, though Cal is more interested in buying a new car. Shawna helps him to use the Internet but insists on going to the movie she wants to see. In scene 3C, Josh introduces his sister, Jennifer, to Mariana. Jennifer tells everyone about her video from a dating agency.

1 Before you watch

▶▶ **Cultural note**

a
- Read the cultural note with the students and see if anything surprises them.
- Go through the uses of the Internet listed in the cultural note and ask if the students use it in any of the ways listed. For example, ask the students to explain how they manage their bank account on the Internet.
- Discuss which uses of the Internet are the best and most useful.

b
- This exercise presents vocabulary from scenes 3A, 3B and 3C.
- Ask the students to go through the vocabulary in the box, checking anything new in a dictionary. Help them with the pronunciation of answers marked * .

  Note: an *advertising account* is when a company agrees to use your agency.

  Answers: Advertising: a campaign*, an account, a radio ad, an agency, a concept. A car: air-conditioning, mileage*, a V6 engine, a model. A man: average weight*, single, a Gemini*, curly hair*, a good sense of humor, good-looking, professional

- If the students put "a model" in "advertising" as well, accept it.
- If you wish, ask the students to add three more items to each column.

2 Watch for main ideas **11:51 – 16:58**

a
- Have the students look at the adjectives and help them with the meanings and pronunciation. Have them look at the pictures of the people, too, to help them understand.
- Give them time to match the sentences, but don't correct them.
- Have the students watch the video looking at the way the people act – the sentences themselves are not in the video, but the feelings they describe should be clear enough.
- Check their answers.

  Answers: 1d 2b 3e 4a 5c

b
- Discuss with the students how they can work out the people's feelings – their expressions, their tone of voice, perhaps gestures.

◀◀ Rewind the video to 3A 12:07 in preparation for **Watch for details**.

3 Watch for details **Scene 3A: 12:07 – 13:08**

- Play the video for the students to check (✔) the correct answers.
- Explain *Let's wow them!* – slang for "Let's impress them!" and ask them how they could "wow" you in the next lesson, or how you could "wow" them.
- Check their answers.

  Answers: 1c 2a 3b 4b

▶▶ **Scene 3B: 13:10 – 15:21**

- Explain the task to the students and make sure they understand.
- Ask them to write the correct adjective by each sentence.
- Warn the students to listen carefully when Cal is looking at the newspaper, as he just reads out pertinent words.
- The students watch and check their answers.

  Answers: 1 The movie "Her Only Love" is romantic. 2 The first car is expensive. 3 The second car is old. 4 Cal's new job is good. 5 Using the Internet is faster. 6 Dinner is going to be late.

- Ask if the students agree with Cal that there are "guy" movies and "girl" movies, and to give some examples.

▶▶ **Scene 3C: 15:24 – 16:58**

- Before playing the video, ask the students to look at the three pictures and describe the men in them.
- Tell them that Jennifer is going to describe her perfect man, and they have to choose which one is closest. The students watch and choose.
- Check their answers.

  Answers: Man 2 is the closest to what she wants, though not perfect!

- The students could discuss if there's anyone in the class who fits the description!

4 After you watch

Language focus: subject + *be / have* + description
- The students read the description and decide who it is.

  Answer: Cal

- Now ask the students to write descriptions of one of the other characters in this unit. They should do this individually. Monitor as they do it. They could use pages 26 and 27 of the Student's Book to help them with the vocabulary.
- The students read out their descriptions to their partners, or you could ask individual students to read out their descriptions to the class.

Discussion
- Make sure the students understand the situation and the possibilities, i.e. they want to buy a car / meet someone.
- Ask them to rank the methods individually then discuss them in small groups.

16

- To encourage them to exchange opinions in English, you could pre-teach expressions like *Why do you say that?*, *I don't agree*, *Me too*.
- Encourage them to say why they prefer certain methods over others.

5 Communication activity

Turn to page 56 for the *What's the best way of …?* activity.

Video Script   COUNTER 11:51–16:58 ▶ ▶ ▶ ▶

Scene 3A: 12:07 – 13.08

Joan:	New business. The Fruity Fruit company is looking for an agency to develop a campaign to sell Fruity Fruit in the Hispanic markets.
Mariana:	To Spanish-speaking markets here in the United States?
Joan:	Yes, in the United States.
Mariana:	Er, what cities?
Joan:	Boston, Los Angeles, New York, OK? Now listen. We are the perfect agency for this. The *perfect* agency. We can show them concepts for TV ads, radio ads, newspapers, magazines.
Luis:	Sounds like a lot of fun.
Joan:	It will be fun, when we get the account. In three weeks the Fruity Fruit people will be here and I want to show them something spectacular. Let's "wow" them, people!
Shawna:	OK? Got it? Let's *wow* them, people!

Scene 3B: 13:10 – 15:21

Shawna:	Hey, baby.
Cal:	Mmm. Hi. Oh, good. Are you ready to go to the movies?
Shawna:	Yeah, and this is the movie I want to see. "Her Only Love."
Cal:	Shawna, I'm a guy. No guy wants to see a movie called "Her Only Love." Can't we see a different movie?
Shawna:	Fine, then you look in the paper and see if there's a movie you want to see.
Cal:	V-6 engine … air conditioning … only 10,000 miles … $29,000! Forget it. I can't spend that much money. … Leather seats … V-6. Only $4800! … Oh, of course. '91.
Shawna:	So, Cal, what movie do you want to see?
Cal:	I'm still looking, baby. I can't find anything.
Shawna:	Well, I'm not surprised, since the movie section is right here.
Cal:	Shawna. I'm sorry, I just can't think about anything but cars. Now that I *finally* have this good job, I want a decent car! It's my dream!

Shawna:	Then, Cal, you should *get* a good car.
Cal:	That's what I'm trying to do!
Shawna:	So let's look on the Internet. It's much faster.
Shawna:	So you enter your requirements … model of car … make … mileage … and price range … and then you can get the car of your dreams …
Cal:	Hey! That's a great idea!
Shawna:	Yes, and we still have time to see "Her Only Love." It starts at 8:15.
Cal:	No, no, baby, please. Not that. I'll take you out to dinner.
Shawna:	Good, after the movie. A nice, late dinner.
Cal:	Oh, OK.

Scene 3C: 15:24 – 16:58

Mariana:	These are the flavors from the other fruit juice companies, right?
Luis:	That's right. Fruity Fruit's competitors.
Jennifer:	Hey, you guys.
Josh:	Hi, Jennifer. What's up? Mariana, do you know my sister Jennifer?
Mariana:	No, I don't. Hi, Jennifer, nice to meet you.
Jennifer:	Hi, Mariana. It's nice to meet you too.
Josh:	Mariana's from Venezuela. She works with Luis and Shawna at the ad agency.
Jennifer:	Oh, what do you do?
Mariana:	I'm a writer.
Josh:	Hey sis, what you got there?
Jennifer:	A video.
Josh:	Of what?
Jennifer:	Of men.
Josh:	Men?!
Jennifer:	Yes. Young, single men. This is from Good Karma Dating service. I asked for a guy who was healthy … non-smoking … good sense of humor … professional … good-looking, of course … tall, average weight … long, curly hair maybe. I'd prefer a Leo or a Libra … but a Gemini is okay. No Aries!
Josh:	No Aries? Hey, er … what am I?
Jennifer:	You're an Aries.
Josh:	That's what I thought … Thanks a lot!
Mariana:	A video dating service? I never heard of that.
Luis:	I was surprised too. Strange, huh?
Mariana:	Hmmm.

Unit Three 3

Matchmaker

1 Before you watch

▶▶ **Cultural note**

a **Read the text and then discuss the questions.**

Internet use in the U.S. is becoming widespread and people are using it for all sorts of things. As well as the established uses of email and research, people are now using the Internet to find new cars, new houses and even new partners. More and more people are reading newspapers online, as well as doing their shopping, booking movie and theater tickets, managing their bank accounts or finding out what the weather will be like.

1 Do you do any of the activities in the cultural note on the Internet? Which ones?
2 What do you think are the best uses of the Internet?

b **Put the words in the box into the correct column.**

a radio ad	curly hair	a V6 engine	a Gemini	average weight	a campaign
mileage	a model	an account	single	air-conditioning	an agency	a concept
good-looking	professional	a good sense of humor

advertising	a car	a man

2 Watch for main ideas

a **Watch the video. Match the sentence beginnings with the reasons.**

1 Joan is impatient because …
2 Shawna is sarcastic because …
3 Cal is surprised because …
4 Jennifer is embarrassed because …
5 Luis is shocked because …

a she has a video about men.
b Joan speaks in a funny way.
c he's never heard of video dating.
d Mariana asks a stupid question.
e Shawna wants him to watch a romantic movie.

b **How can you work out the way the person feels?**

18

Worksheet
Matchmaker

3 Watch for details

▶▶ Scene 3A

Watch the video and check (✔) the correct answer.

1 Fruity Fruit wants to sell its drinks in
   a) Spain.   b) South America.   c) the USA.

2 Which city does Joan not mention?
   a) Philadelphia   b) Los Angeles   c) New York

3 Which type of ads does Joan want to show the Fruity Fruit people? a) Internet b) TV c) posters

4 How much time do they have to prepare?
   a) three days   b) three weeks   c) three months

▶▶ Scene 3B

a The adjectives in these five sentences are mixed up. For example, the movie "Her Only Love" is *romantic*, not *late*. Move the adjectives into different sentences, so that they make sense.

1 The movie "Her Only Love" is late.
2 The first car is old.
3 The second car is faster.
4 Cal's new job is romantic.
5 Using the Internet is expensive.
6 Dinner is going to be good.

b Watch the video and check.

▶▶ Scene 3C

Watch the video. Which of these three men do you think Jennifer would prefer?

4 After you watch

Language focus: subject + *be* / *have* + description
Which of the people in this unit is this?

He's tall and slim with short black hair. He has a beard and moustache. He's wearing a blue T-shirt and jeans and he has a gold chain around his neck.

Write a similar description of another person in the unit. Use the example as a model. Give your description to your partner. Can he / she recognize the person?

Discussion

Here are some different ways you could find the car or person that is best for you.
Put them in order: 1 = the most useful, 6 = the least useful.

	Car	Person
Reading ads in the newspaper		
Putting an ad in the newspaper		
Surfing the Internet		
Asking your friends to help		
Using an agency		
Asking your parents for their help		

Unit Four 4

Teacher's notes

Cleaning up – Summary

In this unit we see how the friends live! In scene 4A, Shawna complains about the mess that Sara has made, and Mariana finds some mold on a plate. The girls realize that they are all responsible, and decide to keep the place clean. In scene 4B, Jin complains about the mess in his apartment and he claims that he always cleans up. However, Luis finds Jin's smelly tennis shoes in the room, so the three admit that they are all responsible. In scene 4C, the boys and girls clean up their apartments, though the boys are not as strict with their new rules as the girls are!

1 Before you watch

▶▶ **Cultural note**

a ● Have the students read the cultural note.
  ● Ask them if they find the statistics surprising, especially the fact that women still do most of the cleaning up.
  ● The students can discuss the questions in small groups before you open them to the class.
b ● Check that the students understand the vocabulary in the sentences. Teach any they are unsure of by miming.
  ● Have the students work in pairs on the task.
  ● Check the pronunciation of *shelves* and *vacuum*.

  Answers: 1d 2h 3g 4f 5a 6c 7e 8b

c ● This is a review of Unit 4 Lesson 2 (frequency adverbs).
  ● Have the students discuss the household chores in pairs.
  ● If you wish, you could teach the class *slob* (a very lazy, untidy person) and then have the students decide who is "the class slob" based on their answers.

2 Watch for main ideas   17:05 – 22:41

● Tell the students to read the four titles and ask them what they think the unit is about.
● Pre-teach any new vocabulary as necessary, e.g. *mold* (a fungus that grows on rotting food).
● Play the unit through while they match the titles and scenes.
● Check their answers.

  Answers: A4 B1 C2

◀◀ Rewind the video to 4A 17.23 in preparation for **Watch for details**.

3 Watch for details   Scenes 4A & 4B: 17:23 – 21:55

Note: In this unit, scenes 4A and 4B are very close in nature, so there are two exercises focusing on both the scenes.

a ● Play scenes 4A and 4B while the students match the problems with the people responsible.
  ● Check the answers around the class.

  Answers: 1 Sara 2 Mariana 3 Josh 4 Luis 5 Jin

b ● Now ask the students to look at the chart and complete as much as they can.

c ● They can compare with a partner before you check as a class.

  Answers:

	Shawna	Mariana	Sara	Jin	Josh	Luis
1 had friends over last night.			✔			
2 left her jacket on the couch.		✔				
3 left tennis shoes in the living room.	✔	✔				
4 finds mold on a plate.		✔				
5 is reading a newspaper.					✔	
6 studied last night.				✔		
7 left his papers on the table.						✔
8 cooked for friends last night.						✔
9 is afraid to go in the bathroom.				✔		

▶▶ **Scene 4C: 21:58 – 22:41**

a ● This is a short, but very visual scene.
  ● Have the students try to match the halves of the sentences.
b ● Play scene 4C for them to check their answers before checking as a class.

  Answers: 1f 2e 3b 4a 5d 6c

c ● Ask the students which apartment they would prefer to live in. Ask them to give reasons for their answers!

4 After you watch

Language focus: gerunds

● Have the students write the number of the activity by the verb that represents their opinion.
● Make sure they understand *don't mind*.
● Then have them compare their opinions with their partner(s).
● Encourage them to use the language in their answers, e.g. *I love cooking for friends but I hate washing the dishes!*

Role-play

● Have the students work in groups to collect their ideas. The purpose is so that the students can help each other with ideas and vocabulary for the role-play. Tell them not to write anything – they should remember their ideas.
● Then regroup the students so that the new group contains students from each of the original groups. One way to do this is to give each student a letter: A, B or C, and then say, "All the As here, the Bs there," etc.
● All the students can act out their role-play at the same time. Listen and invite the best group to act out their role-play in front of the class.

5 Communication activity

Turn to page 58 for the *Spot the differences* activity.

20

Video Script

COUNTER 17:05–22:41 ▶▶▶▶

Scene 4A: 17:23 – 18:56

Shawna:	Oh yuck! I can't believe it. What a mess! This place is disgusting!
Mariana:	Oh, yeah. This place *is* a mess.
Shawna:	This is enough! We have to talk about this! Sara! Sara!
Sara:	What, what? What's up?
Shawna:	Look at this place.
Sara:	Oh, yeah. It's kind of a mess.
Shawna:	Dirty glasses … There's popcorn on the floor … Plates …
Sara:	Well, yeah, I invited some friends over last night. And I was too tired to clean up.
Shawna:	Oh, look over here! Shoes on the floor … a jacket on the couch … dirty socks …
Sara:	Hey, those clothes are not mine.
Mariana:	Oh, uh, those are mine.
Sara:	And what about this sweatshirt and these tennis shoes, Shawna?
Shawna:	Well, this isn't *that* much stuff. Not that much at all compared to all this stuff!
Mariana:	Well look. We're all making a mess. The party last night. Your clothes … my clothes … newspapers … magazines …
All:	Ew.
Mariana:	Old food … What do you call this stuff, this … uh green stuff?
Sara:	Oh, that's mold. M-O-L-D.
Shawna:	Yeah, that's mold all right.
Mariana:	OK. Well, why don't we try to keep the place clean so that we don't have any more mold?

Scene 4B: 18:59 – 21:55

Jin:	Oh, look at this mess!
Luis:	Hey, Jin. Did you study all night? Must be tired.
Jin:	Yeah, I have a big test. I stayed up most of the night. I *am* tired.
Josh:	Hey, you guys want some juice?
Jin:	Yeah, thanks, Josh. You know, you guys. I've been thinking …
Josh:	Uh-huh …
Jin:	About the apartment.
Luis:	What about it?
Jin:	Look around …
Luis:	It is kind of a mess. But I guess I'm used to it now. I don't see it anymore.
Jin:	Well … look! … You know, there are soccer shoes …
Luis:	A basketball … and soccer balls …
Jin:	A baseball glove … a baseball bat …
Luis:	Old magazines … newspapers …
Jin:	Pizza boxes … and bottles.
Josh:	Hey, hey, wait a minute! This mess isn't *all* mine!
Luis:	Well, I don't know about that …
Josh:	Oh, no? Look over there. Those are all of your papers and bottles.
Luis:	That's my work.
Josh:	And what about the kitchen, huh? It's full of dirty dishes …
Luis:	I cooked dinner for some friends last night …
Josh:	So you … or your friends … should clean it up.
Luis:	Yeah, you're right, Josh.
Jin:	And what about the bathroom? I'm *afraid* to go in to the bathroom! The last time we cleaned it was … who knows? We *never* clean the bathroom!
Josh:	And what about you?
Jin:	Me? What about me?
Josh:	Yeah, don't *you* ever make a mess?
Jin:	No. I never make a mess.
Josh:	You *never* make a mess? Never? Never?
Jin:	If I make a mess, I always clean up. Always.
Luis:	Not always. That's impossible. Usually. Sometimes. Not always.
Jin:	Yes, always! Always.
Luis:	Except the bathroom, right?
Jin:	Well …
Luis:	And … what about these?
Jin:	My tennis shoes.
Luis:	They smell terrible!
Jin:	Yeah, they do.

Scene 4C: 21:58 – 22:41

Mariana:	OK, from now on, we have to clean the kitchen every time we use it …
Sara:	Pick up our clothes all the time …
Shawna:	Vacuum and dust once a week …
Mariana:	And put our things away.
Luis:	Let's wash the dishes every day …
Jin:	Leave our tennis shoes outside the window …
Josh:	And clean the bathroom twice a year!

Unit Four 4

Cleaning up

1 Before you watch

▶▶ **Cultural note**

a **Read the text and then discuss the questions.**

America has a day for everything! And April 7th is National No Housework Day! This is a day when you don't need to wash clothes, cook or clean the house! Of course, for some people (let's call them "men!"), No Housework Day is every day. In a recent American study, 42% of women but only 1% of men said they did all the housework in their household!

1 Who does most of the housework in your home?
2 Do you think men are doing more housework today than in the past?
3 What do you think of the idea of a No Housework Day?

b **Match the verbs with the nouns to produce expressions about housework.**

1 keep	a a mess
2 put away	b the dishes
3 vacuum	c the bathroom
4 dust	d the place clean
5 make	e old pizza boxes
6 clean	f the shelves
7 throw away	g the carpet
8 wash	h your clothes

c **Do you always, usually, or never do the things in part b? Tell your partner.**

2 Watch for main ideas

Watch Unit 4. Match each scene with a title. There is one title you do not need to use.

Scene 4A   1 Boys can't keep things tidy!
Scene 4B   2 Cleaning up
Scene 4C   3 Two apartments in a mess
                4 Rubbish, rubbish and mold!

3 Watch for details

▶▶ **Scenes 4A and 4B**

a **Both apartments are in a mess! Watch scenes 4A and 4B and match the picture to the person responsible for the problem.**

1 popcorn on the carpet   2 clothes on the couch   3 a baseball bat   4 bottles of Fruity Fruit   5 smelly tennis shoes

Mariana   Jin   Luis   Sara   Josh

Worksheet
Cleaning up

b Check the box (✔) for the correct person.

	Shawna	Mariana	Sara	Jin	Josh	Luis
1 had friends over last night.						
2 left her jacket on the couch.						
3 left tennis shoes in the living room.						
4 finds mold on a plate.						
5 is reading a newspaper.						
6 studied last night.						
7 left his papers on the table.						
8 cooked for friends last night.						
9 is afraid to go in the bathroom.						

c Now watch Scenes 4A and 4B again and check your answers.

▶▶ **Scene 4C**

a Now see what they decide to do about the problem. Match the halves of the sentences.

1 We have to clean the kitchen   a every day.
2 Pick up our clothes   b once a week.
3 Vacuum and dust   c twice a year!
4 Let's wash the dishes   d outside the window.
5 Leave our tennis shoes   e all the time.
6 And clean the bathroom   f every time we use it.

b Watch scene 4C again and check your answers.

c Which apartment would you prefer to live in? Why?

4 After you watch

Language focus: gerunds

We use *-ing* after many verbs for liking and disliking. Put the numbers of these actions next to the verb which best describes the way you feel about them.

1 washing clothes   2 dusting   3 cooking for friends   4 washing the dishes
5 cleaning the bathroom   6 vacuuming the carpet   7 tidying the room   8 making the bed
9 working in the garden   10 ironing clothes

love _____   don't like _____

like _____   hate _____

don't mind _____

Role-play

Imagine that you live in an apartment like the ones in the video – it's a mess!

1 In groups, think of five or more problems in the apartment, e.g. there are ten old pizza boxes in the kitchen; there are hairs in the bath.
2 Now make new groups with one person from each original group. Have a conversation like the one on the video.

   A: *What a mess! Look at these hairs in the bath.*
   B: *I'm sorry. I didn't have time to clean it. Anyway, what about this cola can on the floor?*
   C: *Oh, it's mine.*

Unit Five 5

Teacher's notes

Dream date — Summary

In the title, "dream" is used to mean "perfect," so it refers to a perfect date. In scene 5A, Mariana's roommates go out on dates leaving her feeling down. Then Jennifer arrives. In scene 5B, Jennifer shows her the dating video to cheer her up. We see some men describing themselves, but Mariana likes only the last one, Mark (who Jennifer thinks is self-centered). In scene 5C, Mariana and Jennifer discuss Mariana's date with Mark the night before. Mark took her to a fancy restaurant, a show and a club, but it turns out that Jennifer was right – he only talked about himself. Finally, they run into Josh in the park and Mariana is impressed that he is coaching kids and doing a Master's in social work. They join him playing basketball.

1 Before you watch

▶▶ **Cultural note**

a ● Have the students read the note and discuss the questions in pairs or small groups.
b ● Pre-teach any new vocabulary as necessary, e.g. *to go on a date*, *fancy* (elegant).
  ● Have the students discuss the question in small groups.

2 Watch for main ideas   `22:47 – 29:47`

● Have the students look at the sentences again and check (✔) them as they see them on the video.
● Check their answers.

Answers: spending a day at the beach, seeing a romantic movie

Note: Adam in scene 5B talks about going to the movies, but he doesn't mention "romantic" movies. Mariana and Jennifer are going for a walk in the park in scene 5C – of course, they're not on a date, but that's not the question!

◀◀ Rewind the video to 5A 23:03 in preparation for **Watch for details**.

3 Watch for details   `Scene 5A: 23:03 – 24:22`

● Have the students try to do the task first and then watch the video to check.
● Check their answers.

Answers: at a concert – Luis and Sara; at home – Mariana; at a sports game – Cal and Shawna

● Ask the students how Mariana feels in the scene and why. (Down, because she's the only one not on a date.)

▶▶ **Scene 5B: 24:25 – 27:04**

a ● Have the students watch the video and check (✔) the boxes next to Adam or Mark.

Answers: Adam: He likes being outdoors; he doesn't eat meat; he's an architect; he doesn't smoke. Mark: He seems strong; he works for a bank; he's looking for a beautiful woman; he has strong emotions.

b ● Have the students discuss the follow-up questions.

Answer: Jennifer thinks Adam is nice and sweet. Mariana isn't impressed. She thinks Mark is handsome and passionate. She is impressed that he's a successful financial analyst! Jennifer agrees that he's handsome, but finds him self-centered and "full of himself" – in other words, arrogant.

▶▶ **Scene 5C: 27:07 – 29:47**

a ● Pre-teach any new vocabulary as necessary, e.g. *a Master's degree* (a second degree, one where the student usually specializes more).
  ● Have the students watch the scene and mark the statements true or false.
  ● Check their answers. They could correct the false statements.

Answers: 1F (Celine's is very expensive.)   2F (Mark got a reservation quickly.)   3T   4F (Mark talks about himself all the time.)   5T   6F (Josh coaches the children after school and on Saturday mornings.)   7T   8T   9F (Josh teaches Mariana how to play basketball.)

b ● Have the students discuss the follow-up question. There is no absolute answer, but perhaps she realizes she was too naive in believing everything Mark said on the video and perhaps was too influenced by his looks and job. Now she is impressed by Josh and realizes she may have been wrong about him, too. In both cases, she judged from appearances!

4 After you watch

Language focus 1: adjectives
● Have the students look at the adjectives and try to remember who said the sentences (1 Jennifer, 2 Jennifer, 3 Jennifer, 4 Adam, 5 Mark, 6 Jennifer), then complete them.
● Check their answers.

Answers: 1 down   2 perfect   3 curious   4 nervous   5 successful   6 self-centered

Language focus 2: *going to*
● Have the students discuss the predictions in pairs or small groups.
● If the students need help with the grammar, they can look at Student's Book page 47.

Role-play
● Discuss with the class first what kind of person they think Mariana is (e.g. *hardworking*, *fun-loving*, *friendly*).
● In pairs, the students prepare a short ad.
● Each pair can perform their ad for the others if you wish!

5 Communication activity

Turn to page 58 for the *Dating agency* activity.

24

Video Script

Scene 5A: 23:03 – 24:22

Cal:	Hey, Shawna, hurry up, we'll be late.
Shawna:	I'm coming, I'm coming. Do you have the tickets?
Cal:	Yes, I have the tickets. This is going to be a great game!
Shawna:	Bye.
Luis:	Hey, Sara. Ready to go?
Sara:	We're going to hear a band!
Mariana:	Goodnight. Have fun.
Luis:	Goodnight, Mariana.
Mariana:	Who is it?
Jennifer:	It's me, Jennifer.
Mariana:	Oh, hi, Jennifer. Come on in.
Jennifer:	Hi, Mariana. Is my brother here? We were supposed to go to a movie.
Mariana:	No, he's not here.
Jennifer:	Hey, you look kind of down. Is something the matter?
Mariana:	Oh, Jennifer. It's Saturday night. And everyone else has a date …
Jennifer:	Oh! I know how that is. Hey, I just got another tape from Good Karma Dating service. Let's find the perfect guy for you!
Mariana:	No, Jennifer, I don't think so, I really don't want …
Jennifer:	No, really. It's just in my car. I'll go get it. I'll be right back!
Mariana:	No, it's OK, oh, I don't want a video date. No, it's OK, it's OK.

Scene 5B: 24:25 – 27:04

Mariana:	I don't know. I don't know about this …
Jennifer:	Hey, aren't you curious? I mean, don't you want to see who's on the video?
Mariana:	Well, I guess you're right. Sure, let's watch it.
Jennifer:	OK, here we go. And number one is … Adam.
Adam:	Hi, my name is Adam. I'm an architect … I like mountain biking and camping. Anything outdoors. I really like going to the movies. I try to make sure I go at least once or twice a month. Uh, what else can I say … oh, let's see … I'm a vegetarian. I don't eat meat. I do eat fish, though. Uh … what else? I don't smoke, I don't smoke. I'm a little nervous. Sorry.
Jennifer:	Hey, I like him. He's nice.
Mariana:	Oh, I don't know, I don't think he's … you know …
Jennifer:	He's sweet. I think I'd like to meet Adam.
Mariana:	Really?
Jennifer:	Hm hmm.
Mariana:	I don't know.
Another male voice:	I'm actually a horticulturist, which is not to say I'm a miscreant in any way but it is to say that I actually take care of the plants …
Mariana:	No, I don't think I like that one.
Jennifer:	Oh, Mariana, you're very difficult to please! Some of them seemed nice, like that guy Peter.
Mariana:	Peter? No, I don't think so. Well, I think we're coming to the last guy.
Mark:	Hello. I'm Mark. And I'm a successful financial analyst for a major bank.
Mariana:	Wow.
Jennifer:	He's good-looking … but … I don't know … I don't think …
Mark:	On the outside, I seem strong, independent … a rock. But I'm not really a rock at all. Actually on the inside, I have very deep feelings, very strong emotions. I need a woman to share my feelings with, someone warm and beautiful, someone who'll listen to me, someone to love me … Are you that woman? The right woman for me?
Mariana:	Oh, he's very handsome. And passionate.
Jennifer:	Oh, Mariana. I'll admit, he's handsome. But he's *so* full of himself.
Mariana:	Full of himself?
Jennifer:	Yeah. He's self-centered. He's only interested in himself, "me, me, me, me." You know what I mean?
Mariana:	No, but I think you're wrong. Mark has deep feelings.
Jennifer:	He has deep feelings … for himself!
Mariana:	Yeah, but he's handsome! And he has a good job! I'm going to meet him!
Jennifer:	Oh, well Mariana. Good luck.

Scene 5C: 27:07 – 29:47

Jennifer:	So, how was your date with Mark last night?
Mariana:	Well, first we went to Celine's for dinner.
Jennifer:	Celine's! Wow! Pretty fancy!
Mark:	This restaurant is the most exclusive restaurant in town. You wait over a month for a reservation … at least most people do! Not me. They know me here.
Jennifer:	So what did you do after dinner?
Mariana:	Then we went to a show.
Mark:	Mariana, everyone wants to see this show. It's impossible to get tickets, but I got tickets. Third row center. Paid a fortune for them. You are going to love this show …
Jennifer:	So the show was great, right?
Mariana:	Yeah. And then after the show we went dancing.
Jennifer:	Dancing?
Mark:	One thing about me … I don't like to talk about myself, but I'm a great dancer.
Mariana:	Oh, Jennifer, you were right. He only talked about himself. "Me, me, me, me, me." He wasn't fun to be with at all!
Jennifer:	Oh. Hey look, there's Josh! Hey, Josh!
Josh:	Hey, Jennifer. Hey, Mariana.
Mariana:	Are you coaching those kids?
Josh:	Yeah. I coach them after school. And on Saturday mornings … like today.
Mariana:	Is that your job?
Josh:	Well, yeah. It's a part-time job. I work in an after-school program for kids with family problems.
Mariana:	Do you like working with kids with problems?
Josh:	Oh, sure. Some day, I'll work with kids like these full-time … I'm getting a Master's degree in social work.
Mariana:	In social work? You're getting a degree in social work?
Josh:	Yeah. Why are you so surprised?
Mariana:	I don't know. I just didn't think that …
Kid:	Hey, Josh. Watch this!
Josh:	One second. Hey guys, I've got to go. Well hey, you just want to play with us?
Jennifer:	Oh, sure.
Josh:	How about you, Mariana?
Mariana:	Well.
Josh:	It's fun. We'll teach you! Here, catch. Now bounce … dribble … OK? You gotta use one hand …

25

Unit Five 5

Dream date

1 Before you watch

▶▶ **Cultural note**

a Read the text and then discuss the questions.

Millions of Americans use dating services every week to find their ideal man or woman – and they are not embarrassed to talk about it! The market is very competitive. Some agencies give you videos or DVDs and phone numbers of other single people. Other agencies put your details on the Internet and send a text message to your cellphone with the phone numbers of interested people.

1 Are these services popular in your town / country?
2 How do people in your town / country find their ideal man or woman?

b Here are some suggestions for a first date. Which do you think are the best ones?

going to a fancy restaurant
spending a day at the beach
going to a football game
watching a video at home
going to a show at the theater

going for a walk in the park
playing basketball
going dancing
seeing a romantic movie
going to a concert

2 Watch for main ideas

Look again at the activities above. Watch Unit 5. Which two activities are **not** seen or mentioned on the video?

3 Watch for details

▶▶ **Scene 5A**

a How are the friends planning to spend the evening? Check (✔) the correct column.

	at a concert	at home	at a sports game
Cal and Shawna			
Luis and Sara			
Mariana			

b Now watch scene 5A again and check your answers.

▶▶ **Scene 5B**

a Here are two of the men Mariana and Jennifer see on the video. Watch scene 5B again and match the sentences with the correct man.

Adam

Mark

Adam		Mark
☐	He seems strong.	☑
☐	He works for a bank.	☐
☐	He likes being outdoors.	☐
☐	He's looking for a beautiful woman.	☐
☐	He doesn't eat meat.	☐
☐	He's an architect.	☐
☐	He doesn't smoke.	☐
☐	He has strong emotions.	☐

b What do Mariana and Jennifer think of the two men? Do you agree?

Worksheet
Dream date

▶▶ Scene 5C

a Watch scene 5C again and mark these statements T (True) or F (False).

1 Celine's is a cheap restaurant. T ☐ F ☐
2 Mark and Mariana waited a month for the dinner reservation. T ☐ F ☐
3 They went to see a very popular show. T ☐ F ☐
4 Mark doesn't like to talk about himself. T ☐ F ☐
5 She didn't enjoy Mark's company. T ☐ F ☐
6 Josh works with the children every morning. T ☐ F ☐
7 Josh is doing a Master's degree. T ☐ F ☐
8 Mariana is surprised by Josh. T ☐ F ☐
9 Josh teaches Mariana how to play soccer. T ☐ F ☐

b What lesson do you think Mariana learned from this?

4 After you watch

Language focus 1: adjectives
Complete these sentences from the video with the correct adjective from the box.

| perfect   curious   self-centered   successful   down   nervous |

1 You look kind of _____ . Is something the matter?
2 Let's find the _____ guy for you!
3 Aren't you _____ ? I mean, don't you want to see who's on the video?
4 I don't smoke. I don't smoke. I'm a little _____ . Sorry.
5 I'm a _____ financial analyst.
6 He's _____ . He's only interested in himself.

Language focus 2: going to
Look at these predictions about people from the unit.
Do you think they are going to happen?

1 Jennifer is going to go on a date with Adam.
2 Mariana is going to see Mark again.
3 Mark is going to find someone to love him.
4 Mariana is going to look at another dating video.
5 Mariana is going to become good at basketball.
6 Josh is going to work with children full-time.
7 Mariana is going to go on a date with Josh.

Role-play
Imagine that Mariana decides to send a video of herself to the video dating agency.
Prepare a video ad for Mariana, like the ones on Jennifer's video.
e.g. Hi. I'm Mariana. I'm from Venezuela. I'm a little nervous about this ...

Compare your ad with another student. Are they very similar?

Unit Six 6

Teacher's notes

A bad day – Summary

In scene 6A, Joan tells her team that the Fruity Fruit people will be coming tomorrow at ten o'clock, so they need to practice their presentation that evening. Shawna, Mariana and Luis all work hard on the project and seem pleased with what they've done. In scene 6B, they all lose their work when the system goes down. Al tells them not to worry, but he doesn't know when the system will be working again. In scene 6C, Joan tells them they need to stay late and finish the revisions. Cal arrives for his date with Shawna, but she has to cancel it. Instead he gets them some Chinese food. In scene 6D, he goes to get his car to give everyone a ride home, but he can't find it and he thinks it's been stolen. Shawna calls the police, but Luis notices Cal's car outside – he had parked in a different place after bringing back the Chinese food.

1 Before you watch

▶▶ **Cultural note**

a ● Pre-teach any new vocabulary as necessary, e.g. *survey* (a survey is when a large number of people answer the same questionnaire).
● Have the students read the information and discuss the questions in pairs. They could be reminded of this theme from Unit 5 (particularly Student's Book page 32). Students who have been to the U.S. could say whether or not they thought Americans were hard-working.

b ● Have the students work in pairs to match up the sentences.
● They can check answers in pairs before you check as a class.

Answers: 2g 3a 4d 5c 6b 7f 8e

● Have the students look again at the sentences and try to find words with the correct meanings. They will be practicing a useful skill – trying to guess meaning from context.
● Ensure that they know to check the part of speech when they try to find the synonym.

Answers: b edit   c trends   d down   e give someone a ride
f a date   g a proposal   h fix

Note: the meaning of "down" in d is especially used for computer networks.

c ● Give the students some personal examples, e.g. *When I first started at my last school, there was no car park and we had to park in the streets nearby. After my first day, I was so exhausted that I couldn't find my car!*
● Then have them discuss the situations in small groups. Encourage them to think of examples – this will create interest in the task which follows and give them ideas for the writing task after the video.
● Have one or two students tell the class their examples.

2 Watch for main ideas   29:53 – 35:22

● Have the students watch the video and then discuss the question in pairs.
● Check their answers.

Answers: Someone stole your car – Cal thinks someone stole his car, but in fact he just forgot where it was!

◀◀ Rewind the video to 6A 30:09 in preparation for **Watch for details**.

3 Watch for details   Scene 6A: 30:09 – 31:18

● Pre-teach any new vocabulary as necessary, e.g. *trend*, *edit ads*.
● Have the students read the sentences and choose the correct answer as they watch.
● Have the students check their answers in pairs before you check as a class.

Answers: 1 ten o'clock   2 tonight   3 complete   4 loves
5 magazine

▶▶ **Scene 6B: 31:21 – 32:30**

● Have the students read the report first and see if they can underline any of the mistakes.
● Then have them watch the scene again and underline the five mistakes in the report.
● Have them check in pairs.
● As you check the answers, ask the students to say what really happened.

Answers: Corrections are given in brackets: photocopier (server); copying some images (sending some files to the printer); two (four); the weekend (tomorrow); called a company to fix the problem (started to fix the problem).

▶▶ **Scene 6C: 32:33 – 33:59**

● Have the students match up the sentences as they watch and then check with their partner.
● After you've checked their answers, have the students practice saying the expressions.

Answers: 1b 2d 3e 4c 5a

▶▶ **Scene 6D: 34:00 – 35:22**

a ● Have the students read the sentences and try to put them in a logical order.
b ● Play the scene again so they can check their order.
● Check their answers.

Answers: a3 b5 c2 d6 e1 f4

4 After you watch

Language focus: past simple and progressive

a ● Have the students do the exercise using the Grammar builder on page 55 of the Student's Book to help them.

28

- When you check the answers, point out the use of *while* meaning "in the middle of the action."

> **Answers:** 1 told   2 was making   3 was sending   4 went   5 told
> 6 arrived   7 was working   8 went   9 was speaking   10 saw

b ● Remind the students of the discussion they had in *Before you watch*.
   ● Have one student read out the example beginning, and then elicit two or three more examples from the students.

- Have them write in class or for homework. Tell them to use the tenses in the text above to help them.

5 Communication activity

Turn to page 58 for the *Computer trouble* activity.

Review of Units 1–6

If you are using the split edition of *Skyline*, there is a brief Review Unit for Units 1–6. See page 64.

Video Script   COUNTER 29:53–35:22 ▶ ▶ ▶

Scene 6A: 30:09 – 31:18

Joan: OK. The Fruity Fruit people will be here tomorrow at ten o'clock. At six o'clock tonight, we're gonna practice our presentation. We're gonna meet right here. OK?

Mariana: My report on drink buying trends in the Hispanic markets is finished! Those look great. Beautiful. Good work, Luis.

Luis: Thanks. I'm happy with them too. Just a *few* more changes.

Shawna: I have the samples of our work … the information about the company … let's see, what else …

Luis: Your ideas for the TV ads are great …

Mariana: Thanks, Luis. I just have to edit the magazine ads … just a few changes … Those labels are nice …

Luis: So would you like to buy some Fruity Fruit?

Mariana: Definitely. All flavors!

Scene 6B: 31:21 – 32:30

Shawna: I'll just send these files to the printer and … uh oh … hey … hey!

Luis: My files! Where are all my files? They disappeared! They're gone!

Mariana: Shawna? Shawna? Did you do something with the Fruity Fruit files?

Shawna: No, my files are gone too!

Al: Hey, you guys. The system's down.

Shawna: The system just went down. Thanks. Unfortunately, we already know that!

Mariana: All of our work is gone!

Luis: Four hours of work, gone.

Al: Hey, don't blame me. It's not my fault. We need a new server!

Luis: Look, Al, the proposal is due tomorrow. When will the system be working again?

Al: Who knows? Maybe an hour. Three or four. Don't worry, I'm working on it, kids, I'm working on it.

Scene 6C: 32:33 – 33:59

Mariana: Finally! The proposal is done.

Joan: And what do you think of it?

Mariana: Uh … I think it looks great.

Joan: Wonderful! 'Cause I can't *wait* to see it!

Luis: Let's get started!

Joan: OK, OK. We need to … write new copy for the TV ads. Write new print ads. Make new labels for these bottles …

Shawna: But, Joan. We'll be here all *night*.

Joan: Sorry, we need to make all these changes. And I will see you all in the morning. Nine o'clock.

Shawna: Well, you guys. Let's get started.

Cal: Hey, Shawna. Are you ready to go out?

Shawna: Oh, Cal. I'm sorry. I have to cancel our date. We have some last-minute changes. We have to work late.

Cal: Oh, that's too bad. But hey, I'll go out, get some Chinese food for everybody, how about that?

Luis: Cal, thanks a lot. That sounds great.

Mariana: Thanks, Cal. I'm really hungry.

Cal: Great, I'll be right back!

Shawna: Thank you, sweetie.

Mariana: That was delicious. I feel much better now.

Luis: Thanks for going out, Cal.

Cal: No, no problem. I'm happy to do it.

Scene 6D: 34:00 – 35:22

Luis: OK, here's the last ad. Looks great.

Mariana: Where's Cal?

Shawna: He went down to get the car. He's going to give us a ride home.

Mariana: Oh, how nice of him.

Cal: My car! My car! Somebody stole it! I can't believe this.

Shawna: What?

Cal: I can't believe this!

Shawna: Your car?

Cal: My new car. Gone. Stolen! This is terrible!

Shawna: Let's call the police …

Mariana: Where did you park your car?

Cal: I parked out there. See? Look: no cars.

Shawna: Hello, I'd like to report a stolen vehicle … yes, I'll hold.

Mariana: Look Cal … uh … Maybe they'll find it.

Cal: No, no. They won't find it. They'll never find it. It's gone.

Shawna: Yes, officer. It was in front of our office. Somebody stole the car while we were working … we were talking a lot and we didn't hear anything. Yes, we'll wait here for an officer to come. The address is …

Luis: Hey, Cal. Isn't that your car up there?

Cal: Let me see. Hey, I don't believe it! It is my car! It's in the back …

Mariana: When you went to pick up the Chinese food …

Cal: Oh, yeah! When I brought the food back I parked it in a different place!

Shawna: Oh, officer. Uh, never mind. We just found the car. Yeah, he forgot where he parked it. Sorry. Thanks. Goodnight.

Unit Six 6

A bad day

1 Before you watch

▶▶ **Cultural note**

a Read the text and then discuss the questions.

In a recent survey, 46% of Americans felt they were working too much. One in four American workers said they spent more than 50 hours per week at work. Women, in particular, felt they were having to work too many hours. Many workers felt they were making more mistakes at work as a result of overwork and were unhappy that they couldn't spend enough time with their families and friends.

1 How many hours per week do people usually work in your country?
2 When people work extra hours, do they normally get more money?

b 1 Match the beginnings of the sentences with the correct endings.

1 It's important to identify	a because the server's down.
2 You need to edit the ads	b a ride home.
3 We can't use the computers right now	c our date. I have too much work.
4 I have to work all night because the proposal	d is due tomorrow morning.
5 I'm sorry but I have to cancel	e will it cost to fix it?
6 Don't call a taxi. I can give you	f my car. I parked it outside my house.
7 Call the police. I think someone stole	g before you send them to the printer.
8 My computer is broken. How much	h new trends in the market.

2 Now find words in the sentences with these meanings.

a must be finished *is due*	e take someone in your car
b make changes to a text	f a romantic meeting
c new developments	g a paper offering to work on a project
d not working	h repair

c Tell your partners about a time when:

you worked all night on a project.
you lost work on your computer.
you forgot where you parked your car.

someone told you your work was great.
someone stole your car.
you cancelled a date because you were busy.

2 Watch for main ideas

Look again at the six events above. You will see all of them in the video except one: which one doesn't happen?

3 Watch for details

▶▶ Scene 6A

Watch scene 6A again and choose the correct answer.

1 The Fruity Fruit people will arrive at *six o'clock / ten o'clock*.

2 They're going to practice the presentation *tomorrow morning / tonight*.

3 Mariana's report is *complete / incomplete*.

4 Luis *loves / doesn't like* Mariana's work.

5 Mariana has to edit the *TV / magazine* ads.

PHOTOCOPIABLE

Copyright © Macmillan Publishers Limited 2002.

Worksheet
A bad day

▶▶ Scene 6B

There are five mistakes in Al's Problem Report. Watch scene 6B again and underline them.

Problem Report
There was another problem with the photocopier today. Shawna was just copying some images when the system went down! Shawna, Mariana and Luis each lost about two hours of work. It was important because they needed to finish the project before the weekend. I called a company to fix the problem, but I don't know how long it will take.

▶▶ Scene 6C

Watch Scene 6C again and match the people with things they say in this scene.

1 We'll be here all night.   a Joan
2 That sounds great!   b Shawna
3 I feel much better now!   c Cal
4 Are you ready to go out?   d Luis
5 I can't wait to see it!   e Mariana

▶▶ Scene 6D

a In Scene 6D Cal thinks someone has stolen his car. Put the events from Scene 6D into the correct order.

a Shawna calls the police.	
b Mariana remembers why the car is in a different place.	
c Cal says he can't find his car.	
d Shawna says sorry to the police officer.	
e Shawna says that Cal will drive everyone home.	1
f Luis sees Cal's car outside.	

b Now watch scene 6D again and check your answers.

4 After you watch

Language focus: past simple and progressive

a Read this summary of Unit 6 and choose the correct tenses.

Joan (1) *told / was telling* everyone to finish their work by six o'clock. Everyone was confident but when Mariana (2) *made / was making* some final changes and Shawna (3) *sent / was sending* the files to the printer, the system (4) *went / was going* down. Al (5) *told / was telling* them not to worry. When Cal (6) *arrived / was arriving*, Shawna (7) *worked / was working* and had to cancel their date. Later, Cal offered everyone a ride home and he (8) *went / was going* to get his car. He couldn't find it, but while Shawna (9) *spoke / was speaking* to the police, Luis (10) *saw / was seeing* Cal's car outside. It wasn't a bad day after all!

b Choose one of the situations you spoke about in "Before you watch." Write about 150 words and try to include all of these points:

What were you doing at the time?   Why did it happen?
How did you and the other people feel?   What happened in the end?

Start like this: *I'll never forget the time I (lost about a week's work on the computer!) I was (working on a college essay at the time …)*

Unit Seven 7

Teacher's notes

Review of Units 1–6

If you are using the split edition of *Skyline*, there is a brief Review Unit for Units 1–6 of the video. See page 64.

Play-off game — Summary

A play-off game is an important game of American football near the end of the season. The winner goes on to play in the final. In scene 7A, the narrator explains the difference between football and soccer in America. In scene 7B, Josh, Jennifer, Shawna and Cal are watching a football game on TV. They try to explain the rules to Mariana but she isn't impressed. The team is playing badly at the beginning and everyone is tense. Things begin to improve and they get excited. Jin comes in and asks them to be less noisy, but they continue making noise, so Mariana invites him to study in her apartment. The scene ends with a touchdown and the friends celebrate.

1 Before you watch

▶▶ **Cultural note**

a ● Pre-teach any new vocabulary as necessary, e.g. *spectator sport* (a sport that people watch), *professional* (of sport – to play a sport as one's job).
● Ask the students if they have seen any American football on TV. If so, ask them to explain what they know about it.
● Discuss the questions in small groups, then as a class.

b ● The students may have no idea about American football, but this vocabulary will be useful in understanding the unit.
● The students read the definitions and use their common sense to match them with the expressions. Note that not every player is a quarterback! The quarterback is the most important player in an American football team – he directs the attack on the opposing team.
● Check their answers.

> **Answers:** 2d 3f 4e 5a 6c

2 Watch for main ideas   36:50 – 40:56

● Have the students read the statements and check that they understand them.
● Play the video through so they can mark T or F as they watch.
● Check their answers. When you check number 4, ask the students if they are surprised or if they usually watch sports matches together with male and female friends.
● If you wish, ask the students to correct the false statements.

> **Answers:** 1T 2T 3F (Their team is losing and they aren't enjoying the game at first.) 4F (The girls are interested too.) 5T 6T

◀◀ Rewind the video to 7A 37:05 in preparation for **Watch for details**.

3 Watch for details   Scenes 7A: 37:05 – 37:50

● Have the students read the passage and underline the words they think are wrong. Tell them that one of the words is replaced by one with a very similar pronunciation.
● Then have them watch the scene with their books closed.
● They can then circle the different words.
● They can watch again with books open to check their answers. Check that they understand *passion* (a fierce love and commitment).

> **Answers:** boring ➔ popular, walking ➔ running, your hands ➔ your head, rugby ➔ soccer, crazy ➔ different, fairly ➔ very, unpopular ➔ popular, fashion ➔ passion

▶▶ **Scene 7B: 37:53 – 40:56**

a ● Have the students try to match the sentences to the pictures before watching, using the expressions on the characters' faces to help them.
b ● Then play the scene for them to check their answers.

> **Answers:** 1E 2C 3D 4A 5B

c ● The next part of the exercise focuses on some of the grammar from Unit 7 of the Student's Book. Tell the students to use their knowledge of English to choose the correct words to complete the sentences.
● Have them watch the scene again if you wish before you check their answers.

> **Answers:** 1a 2c 3c 4b 5b

● Point out the following: in 2 we would need *being* with *Do you mind*; in 3 we can't use the comparative after *very*; in 4 *would you like* is used for an offer – *Do you like* is used to ask about general tastes; in 5 *much* or *a lot* can be used for emphasis with comparatives.

4 After you watch

Language focus: comparatives

● Pre-teach any new vocabulary as necessary, e.g. *working out* (doing exercises in a gym), *healthy* (in good physical condition).
● Give some more examples including comparatives with *more* and *-er*. If necessary, refer students to page 63 of the Student's Book.
● Have the students play the game in groups. Listen and note correct and incorrect comparatives you hear during the activity. At the end, write these examples on the board and have the students decide whether they are correct or incorrect.
● Ask the students at the end to give the best reasons they heard in their groups for one sport being better than another.

5 Communication activity

Turn to page 60 for the *Find someone who …* activity.

32

Video Script COUNTER 36:50–40:56 ▶▶▶

Scene 7A: 37:05 – 37:50

Narrator: The game of football is one of the most popular games in the world. Most people know football to be a game of running and moving the ball down the field with your feet and sometimes your head. However, in America that game is usually called soccer. Football to Americans is an entirely different sport. People in the United States take American football very seriously. The sport is wildly popular in the U.S. Many Americans follow their football teams with the same passion that people around the world follow their hometown soccer teams.

Scene 7B: 37:53 – 40:56

Josh: I can't believe it! We're down by seven points at half-time.

Jennifer: Oh, I know, these guys are terrible! Come on, play football!

Josh: Evans is the worst quarterback we've ever had …

Mariana: Josh, I don't understand this game at all … Would you pass the popcorn?

Josh: Here you go … Er … OK, look. Here's the field …

Mariana: Field … how long is the field?

Josh: 100 yards long.

Mariana: Yards. More or less like meters, right?

Josh: Yeah, I think so. Here is one end-zone. Here is the other end-zone. A player needs to get into the end-zone to score a touchdown.

Mariana: Touchdown?

Josh: Er yeah, points. A touchdown is six points.

Mariana: Er, so it's like a goal, right?

Cal: Right. In soccer we say goal but in football we say touchdown.

Mariana: Well, I think soccer's a lot easier to understand than football!

Cal: Not to us!

Josh: Wow, look at this kick-off return! Go, go!

Cal: I don't believe it!

Shawna: Touchdown!

Josh: They got the extra point!

Jennifer: The score is tied! Yes!

Mariana: I like it when they kick the ball!

Jin: Hey …uh … guys … Maybe … uh … Could you be a little quieter? I'm trying to finish this work …

Josh: Oh, sure, sure. Yeah, yeah. Sorry about that.

Jennifer: All right you guys, this is a big play …

Cal: You can do it. Yeah! You got it!

Jin: Please, please, can you keep it down? Do you mind? It's very hard for me to work with all this noise.

Shawna: Oh, sorry. Sorry.

Josh: No, no. An interception! I can't believe it! Terrible!

Jennifer: That was just such a terrible pass!

Cal: I'm switching teams.

Mariana: Hey, hey, hey, you guys, Jin is trying to study! Please be a little quieter.

Jin: Mariana, it's OK. Don't worry about it. Never mind …

Mariana: Look, Jin. I know your work is important. Listen … would you like to work in our apartment? It's a lot quieter over there.

Jin: Do you mind?

Mariana: No, really I don't mind. Come on, let's go!

Jin: All right. Hey … Thanks a lot.

Mariana: You know, soccer is really a much better game.

Jin: Yes, but they don't understand that.

All: Touchdown!

33

Unit Seven 7

Play-off game

1 Before you watch

▶▶ **Cultural note**

a Read the text and then discuss the questions.

American football is the most popular spectator sport in the United States. The game started in American universities more than 100 years ago and it is still a very important part of university life. Major American colleges have stadiums for 50,000 people or more. Americans often invite their friends over to watch important games, especially the Super Bowl – the final between the champions of the two professional leagues. More than half of the American population and 750 million people all over the world watch this game on TV!

1 How important is sport in colleges in your country?
2 Which are the best and worst sports to watch on TV?

b Match the expressions on the left with their meanings on the right.

1 They scored a touchdown.   a Give the ball to another player.
2 It's half-time.   b They put the ball in the end-zone.
3 The game is tied.   c The game is starting.
4 He's a great quarterback.   d It's the middle of the game.
5 Pass the ball.   e He's a very good player.
6 It's the kick-off.   f No team is winning.

2 Watch for main ideas

The friends are watching a football match. Read the statements and mark each one T (True) or F (False).

		T	F
1	American football is different from soccer.	☐	☐
2	American football is very popular in the United States.	☐	☐
3	The friends are enjoying the game at first.	☐	☐
4	Only the boys are interested in the game.	☐	☐
5	Jin wants everyone to be quieter.	☐	☐
6	The friends are enjoying the game at the end.	☐	☐

3 Watch for details

▶▶ **Scene 7A**

a This is the introduction to the unit, but eight words are different. Circle the different words.

The game of football is one of the most boring games in the world. Most people know football to be a game of walking and moving the ball down the field with your feet and sometimes your hands. However, in America that game is usually called rugby. Football to Americans is an entirely crazy sport. People in the United States take American football fairly seriously. The sport is wildly unpopular in the U.S. Many Americans follow their football teams with the same fashion that people around the world follow their hometown soccer teams.

b Now watch scene 7A again to check your answers.

PHOTOCOPIABLE

34   Copyright © Macmillan Publishers Limited 2002.

Worksheet
Play-off game

▸▸ **Scene 7B**

a Match the pictures with what the people are saying.

1 I'm switching teams.
2 Could you be a little quieter?
3 Terrible!
4 Come on, play football!
5 I don't understand this game at all.

b Now watch scene 7B and check your answers.

c Choose the correct words to complete the sentences.

1 **Mariana:** I think soccer's a lot _____ to understand than football.
 a) easier   b) easy   c) difficult

2 **Jin:** _____ be a little quieter?
 a) Do you mind   b) Would you like   c) Could you

3 **Jin:** It's very _____ for me to work with all this noise.
 a) harder   b) easier   c) hard

4 **Mariana:** _____ to work in our apartment?
 a) Do you like   b) Would you like   c) Do you mind

5 **Mariana:** You know, soccer is really a much _____ game.
 a) interesting   b) better   c) exciting

4 After you watch

Language focus: comparatives

Play this game in groups. Compare the activities below, starting with tennis.
Each player makes a comparison and gives a reason for it.

Player 1:   Tennis is more sociable than swimming.
Player 2:   Why do you say that?
Player 1:   Because you can't speak when you're swimming!
Player 3:   Swimming is more exciting than cycling.
Player 1:   Why do you say that?

Each player starts with ten points. If you don't have a good reason, you lose one point. The winner is the player with the most points at the end.

tennis → swimming → cycling → skiing → dancing → working out → surfing → playing computer games

Here are some adjectives you can use:

expensive   exciting   dangerous   healthy   good   easy   beautiful   noisy   sexy   sociable

Unit Eight 8

Teacher's notes

Presidents' Day weekend – Summary

In this unit we learn about Presidents' Day and the friends decide to go skiing together during the holiday. In scene 8A, we find out what Presidents' Day is and how Americans often celebrate it. In scene 8B, a TV commercial for Eagle Mountain makes Mariana think about going skiing and the others persuade her to go with them for Presidents' Day weekend. In scene 8C, Josh and Jennifer come in and Josh is very keen on the idea of going, especially when he sees that Mariana is interested in him, but he has to beg Jennifer to let him go, because they're supposed to visit their uncle Bob to celebrate his birthday and the holiday with their family.

1 Before you watch

▶▶ **Cultural note**

a ● Have the students read the cultural note.
  ● Help them with the vocabulary if necessary. Give examples of holidays in your country that "honor" historical figures.
  ● Discuss the questions as a class. Does the students' country have more or fewer national holidays than the U.S?
  ● If you or your students wish to have more information on American national holidays, try the website: http://usinfo.state.gov/usa/infousa/facts/factover/holidays.htm
b ● This exercise will help the students with the ski-related vocabulary that they will encounter in this unit.
  ● Have the students write the correct words under the pictures.
  ● Help the students with the pronunciation of the new vocabulary.

  Answers: 1 snowboarding   2 skiing   3 skis   4 a trail   5 a lodge
  6 gloves   7 goggles

  ● Make sure the students are clear about the meanings of each of the words: *snowboarding* is like surfing on snow. In fact, the original snowboarders used adapted surfboards! A *trail* is a mountainside that has been specially prepared for skiing and a *lodge* is a small hotel in a ski resort.
c ● Pre-teach any new vocabulary as necessary, e.g. *tiring* (something that makes you tired).
  ● Have the students talk in pairs or small groups.
  ● The students can either use their own experience or their imagination.
  ● Ask the students who have been skiing to tell the class about their experiences.

2 Watch for main ideas   41:01 – 45:10

  ● Have the students read the statements before they watch and make sure they understand them.
  ● Play the unit through once.
  ● Then have them check their answers in pairs.
  ● Check their answers and ask the students if they can correct the false statements.

  Answers: 1F (It honors Presidents Washington and Lincoln.)
  2F (People often go skiing.)   3T   4T   5F (They decide to spend a weekend skiing.)   6T   7F (He doesn't want to visit his cousins.)
  8F (She decides to visit their cousins.)

◀◀ Rewind the video to 8A 41:17 in preparation for **Watch for details**.

3 Watch for details   Scene 8A: 41:17 – 42:16

a ● Have the students match the sentences. They should be able to match most of them before watching the video by using their common sense and grammatical clues.
  ● They can then watch the scene again and check their answers.
b ● Allow them to check in pairs before you check the answers with the whole class.

  Answers: 1d 2c 3a 4f 5e 6b

▶▶ **Scene 8B: 42:16 – 43:03**

  ● The scene is short and the characters speak fast so the students will have to pay close attention.
  ● If necessary, remind them who Mariana, Cal and Jin are.
  ● Pre-teach any new vocabulary as necessary, e.g. *take ... off*, as in *take Friday off* (take a day's vacation from work).
  ● Have them check (✔) the correct column as they watch.
  ● When you've checked their answers, have the students practice saying some of the expressions.

  Answers: 1 Mariana   2 Cal   3 Mariana   4 Jin   5 Mariana   6 Jin
  7 Cal   8 Mariana

▶▶ **Scene 8C: 43:05 – 45:10**

  ● Have the students read the questions. Pre-teach any new vocabulary as necessary, e.g. *Have a seat* (sit down). Tell the students that Connecticut is a state in the northeastern United States, south of Boston.
  ● The students watch the scene again and mark the correct answer.
  ● If you wish, you could explain that *pretty please* is a childish way of saying *please*. Josh is probably being a little bit ironic – but it works!

  Answers: 1b 2a 3c 4a 5b

4 After you watch

Language focus: *too* and *either*
  ● This exercise gives provides extra practice of page 73 of the Student's Book.
  ● Look at the examples together with the students.
  ● Have them do the exercise then compare their answers with their partners before you check them as a class.

  Answers: 1 ... do too.   2 ... doesn't either.   3 ... does too.
  4 ... can too.   5 ... are too.

Discussion
  ● Read through the questions with the students and ask them to discuss the first two questions in pairs.
  ● Monitor and find out their opinions, and their reasons.
  ● Discuss the third question as a class – the answers to the first two will have prepared the students for this. Encourage debate about the importance of family in general.

5 Communication activity

Turn to page 60 for the *Agreement* activity.

36

Video Script COUNTER 41:01–45:10

Scene 8A: 41:17 – 42:16

Narrator: What is Presidents' Day anyway? Presidents' Day is always on the 3rd Monday of February. It's a national holiday. Presidents' Day is a combined holiday that honors two American presidents: George Washington and Abraham Lincoln. Both men were born in February. Abraham Lincoln was born on February 12th, George Washington born on February 22nd. Today, many people celebrate the holiday by going skiing; many other people go shopping. Presidents' Day is a time for buying a car or going to big sales in stores. Presidents' Day weekend is coming and it's a great time to get away to Eagle Mountain and the Eagle Mountain Lodge.
Ski Eagle Mountain's beautiful trails all day … Enjoy the beautiful winter wonderland of Eagle Mountain. Make your reservations today for Presidents' Day weekend at the Eagle Mountain Lodge.

Scene 8B: 42:16 – 43:03

Mariana: Wow! Skiing! It looks like fun. I'd like to try it …

Cal: I'd like to go skiing, too. Let's go. Let's do it. Look, Monday's a holiday. We could take Friday off, that's four days …

Shawna: Yeah, we can leave Thursday night after work … ski all day Friday … all day Saturday …

Mariana: Wait, wait. I didn't really mean we should go. I can't ski. I've never skied …

Jin: Oh, that's no problem, Mariana. You can learn to ski – one lesson. Really.

Mariana: Oh, Jin. I don't think so. One lesson?

Shawna: Oh, no. It's true. You can learn to ski really fast. Skiing is the easiest sport to learn.

Jin: It's true. You take one class in the morning. Then by the afternoon you'll be skiing some of the easier trails. It's so much fun.

Shawna: Yeah, it's really fun.

Cal: So what do you think? Do you want to try it?

Mariana: Sure. Why not? If it's really easy to learn.

Scene 8C: 43:05 – 45:10

Josh: Hi, you guys.

Mariana: Hi, Josh. Hi, Jennifer.

Shawna: OK. Have a seat.

Cal: We're going skiing for Presidents' Day Weekend.

Josh: You are? Where are you going?

Jin: Well, we were thinking about Eagle Mountain. It's the closest place.

Mariana: Do you want to come?

Josh: Yeah, sure! Skiing and snowboarding! I'd *love* to go.

Mariana: You should come! You can help me practice skiing … if you don't mind.

Josh: Sure. I'll help you. You're pretty athletic. I'd … you'll learn fast.

Jennifer: Uh, Josh, wait a minute. I think you're forgetting something.

Josh: What, what …

Jennifer: Uncle Bob?

Josh: Uncle Bob?

Jennifer: Yeah, remember. It's Uncle Bob's birthday. We're supposed to go to Connecticut that weekend.

Josh: Connecticut … no, I, I don't want to go …

Jennifer: Grandma and all of the cousins are going to be there …

Josh: The cousins! Cammie and Derek? Those cousins? Oh … No thanks.

Jennifer: Cammie and Derek are not that bad.

Josh: Yes, they are. You know they are.

Jennifer: No, they aren't.

Josh: Oh, you lie! You don't like them either. You know how Derek makes you crazy – talking about how much money he has. Money, money, money. And he has no sense of humor … and Cammie … I mean Cammie, I just want …

Jennifer: Hey, OK, OK, all right, all right. They're terrible. But still it's a family obligation … and if you don't go, then I have to be with them alone.

Josh: You don't have to go, either.

Jennifer: Yes, I do.

Josh: No, you don't, sis. Come with us.

Jennifer: No, because if you don't go, then I really *have* to go.

Josh: Jen, come on. Please. I want to go skiing. And look, Mariana is *finally* starting to like me. She smiled at me! Please.

Jennifer: Oh …

Josh: Pretty please …

Jennifer: Josh …

Josh: Pretty please with sugar on top?

Jennifer: Oh, all right, go ahead, have fun. I'll tell Cammie that you miss her …

Unit Eight 8

Presidents' Day weekend

1 Before you watch

▶▶ **Cultural note**

a Read the text and then discuss the questions.

The United States has eleven national holidays. Two very famous American holidays are Independence Day on July 4th and Thanksgiving on the fourth Thursday in November. Thanksgiving is a time to spend with your family and remember good times, so many people take vacation time on the Friday too. Most of the other holidays are on Mondays. Three of them honor famous people from history: Martin Luther King Day – the third Monday of January; Presidents' Day – the third Monday in February and Columbus Day – the second Monday in October.

1 How many national holidays are there in your country?
2 What is your favorite holiday? Why?

b Find the correct word in the box below and write it next to the picture.

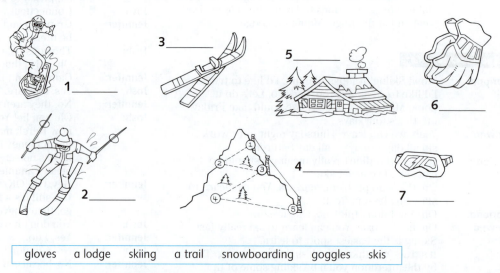

| gloves   a lodge   skiing   a trail   snowboarding   goggles   skis |

c In this unit, the friends are talking about going skiing. Tell your partner if you think skiing is:

easy   expensive   fun   dangerous   tiring   boring

2 Watch for main ideas

Read the statements. Watch Unit 8 and mark each one T (True) or F (False).

1 Presidents' Day honors President Kennedy and President Roosevelt.   T ☐   F ☐
2 People often go to the beach on Presidents' Day weekend.   T ☐   F ☐
3 Mariana can't ski.   T ☐   F ☐
4 Jin and Shawna think skiing is very easy.   T ☐   F ☐
5 They decide to spend a week skiing.   T ☐   F ☐
6 Mariana wants Josh to come with them.   T ☐   F ☐
7 Josh wants to visit his cousins.   T ☐   F ☐
8 Jennifer decides to go skiing with them.   T ☐   F ☐

8 Worksheet
Presidents' Day weekend

3 Watch for details

▶▶ **Scene 8A**

a Match the beginnings and endings of the sentences.

1 Presidents' Day is always on	a February 12th.
2 Presidents' Day is a	b get away to Eagle Mountain.
3 Abraham Lincoln was born on	c holiday that honors two presidents.
4 George Washington was born on	d the third Monday of February.
5 Presidents' Day is a time for	e buying a car.
6 It's a great time to	f February 22nd.

b Now watch scene 8A again and check your answers.

▶▶ **Scene 8B**

Who says what? Watch scene 8B again and check (✔) the correct person.

	Mariana	Cal	Jin
1 I'd like to try it.	✔		
2 Let's do it.			
3 Wait. Wait.			
4 Oh, that's no problem.			
5 I don't think so.			
6 It's so much fun.			
7 So what do you think?			
8 Why not?			

▶▶ **Scene 8C**

Watch scene 8C again and choose the correct answer (a, b or c).

1 They choose Eagle Mountain because it's a) the cheapest.   b) the closest.   c) the coldest.

2 Whose birthday is it? a) Uncle Bob's   b) Cousin Derek's   c) Grandma's

3 Who does Josh dislike? a) Cammie   b) Derek   c) Cammie and Derek

4 Josh thinks that Mariana a) likes him.   b) is crazy about him.   c) needs him.

5 How many times does Josh say "Please?" a) twice   b) four times   c) six times

4 After you watch

Language focus: *too* **and** *either*

Complete the second sentence in each pair, using *too* **or** *either* **to show agreement.**

Example: *Cal is going to Eagle Mountain. Josh is going too.*
Josh doesn't want to go to Connecticut. Jennifer doesn't either.

1 Mariana wants to go skiing. The others _____ .

2 Shawna doesn't think skiing is difficult. Jin _____ .

3 Jin thinks skiing is fun. Shawna _____ .

4 Jin can ski. Josh _____ .

5 Grandma is going to be there. The cousins _____ .

Discussion

Josh and Jennifer had different ideas about the importance of a family celebration. Discuss these questions:

1 Do you think Josh is selfish because he puts his own wishes first?

2 Do you think Jennifer is right to go to a celebration that she knows she won't enjoy?

3 Do you think family celebrations are important? Why? / Why not?

Copyright © Macmillan Publishers Limited 2002.

PHOTOCOPIABLE

39

Unit Nine 9 — Teacher's notes

Pain in the neck – Summary

The title "Pain in the neck" has a literal meaning and may express the kind of pain that Josh feels in this unit, but we also use it for a thing or person that annoys us! In this unit, we see the friends on the skiing weekend they planned in Unit 8. In scene 9A, we are introduced to the Japanese massage technique of Shiatsu. Scene 9B takes place in the ski lodge after a day's skiing. Mariana has had a good first day's skiing, but Josh comes in with a sore shoulder after falling. Jin suggests having a Shiatsu massage. Josh is sceptical at first but finally agrees. In scene 9C, we see Josh having his Shiatsu – it hurts but it works!

1 Before you watch

▶▶ **Cultural note**

a ● Pre-teach any new vocabulary as necessary, e.g. *massage* (manipulating and stroking the body), *herbal medicine* (medicine made from only natural ingredients), *homeopathy* (a therapy based on giving the patient small amounts of the substance that could be causing the problem).
  ● The students read the cultural note and discuss the questions in pairs or groups.
  ● Have the students with more knowledge or experience of alternative medicine tell the other students about it.
  ● Students with little knowledge or interest may prefer to discuss the topics in **c** after the crossword.

b ● Have the students do the crossword in pairs, using the clues and the words in the box.
  ● Help them with the pronunciation of *headache, shoulder, massage* and *pressure*.
  ● Check answers by asking the students to draw and complete the crossword on the board.

> **Answers:** Across – 4 headache, 6 needle, 7 massage, 9 relieve 10 pressure; Down – 1 shoulder, 2 pain, 3 take, 5 energy, 8 saves

c ● Have the students discuss these topics in pairs or small groups.
  ● Then ask them to volunteer a few of the interesting answers to discuss with the class.

2 Watch for main ideas
45:16 – 49:25

a ● Pre-teach any new vocabulary as necessary, e.g. *nonsense* (something worthless, without sense).
  ● They watch Unit 9 and choose the correct answers.
  ● Have them compare their answers with their partner before you check as a class.

> **Answers:** 1a 2b 3c 4c 5b

b ● Discuss the question as a class.

◀◀ Rewind the video to 9A 45:31 in preparation for **Watch for details**.

3 Watch for details
Scene 9A: 45:31 – 46:21

● This scene is a short introduction to Shiatsu. The exercise asks the students about the meanings of some Japanese words, but they are explained clearly on the video.
● The scene includes some quite technical vocabulary about massage, which is not worth focusing on at this level, but point out that acupuncture is the placing of fine needles at various points in the skin.
● Have the students try to match the words and meanings as they watch.
● Check their answers.

> **Answers:** 1d 2c 3b 4a

▶▶ **Scene 9B: 46.24 – 48.42**

● Pre-teach any new vocabulary as necessary, e.g. *hooey* (nonsense), *relieves stress* (makes you feel less stressed), *a hot tub* (a hot bath).
● Make sure that the students understand the task: they should work out who the pronouns in bold refer to, not who says the sentence.
● If possible, play the first part and show how the example works, i.e. Cal says the sentence, but the word *you* refers to Mariana.
● The students can watch the video with their books open and then check in pairs as for the other tasks.

> **Answers:** 2 Mariana 3 Mariana 4 Josh 5 Josh 6 Jin 7 Jin
> 8 Mariana 9 Josh

▶▶ **Scene 9C: 48:46 – 49:25**

● Have the students read the summary and try to find the six mistakes from memory.
● They should correct them if they can.
● Then they watch scene 9C and check their answers.

> **Answers:** feels very good ➜ feels terrible or hurts a lot, the man ➜ the woman, hurt later ➜ get better, feel worse ➜ feel better, it's terrible ➜ it's great, swimming ➜ snowboarding

4 After you watch

Language focus: *should / need to / have to*

a ● This exercise gives the students further practice with the grammar on page 83 of the Student's Book.
  ● Have the students match the sentences in pairs. Tell them that there may be more than one combination but to be careful with the grammar.
  ● Have them compare with their partner before you check the answers with the whole class.

> **Most likely answers:** 1 c, f 2 a, b 3 d, e

40

b
- Have the students work in pairs – keeping their sport a secret.
- Each pair chooses a sport and writes their six sentences.
- Give them an example to show that they shouldn't make the sport too obvious. For example, give them the sentences: *You have to run a lot. You should pass the ball when it's possible. You sometimes need to use your head.* and see if they can guess it's soccer.

- The students could tell the whole class their sentences or move around the class seeing if other pairs can guess.

5 Communication activity

Turn to page 60 for the *Rules and advice* activity.

Scene 9A: 43:31 – 46:21

Narrator: Shiatsu is a massage technique and is similar to acupuncture. Shiatsu is a Japanese word, "shi" meaning finger and "atsu" meaning pressure. But Shiatsu is more than acupressure. It is a combination of different techniques including grasping, pressing, sweeping, rotating, padding and even walking on the person's back, legs and feet. Natural body weight is used to apply pressure on certain points on the body. The energy that passes through this pressure is called "Chi." Chi is the origin, the power of life. Traditionally everything was seen as an expression of Chi.

Scene 9B: 46:22 – 48:42

Jin: Hey look, there's a race tomorrow. Mariana, why don't you enter?
Cal: Yeah, Mariana, after your skiing today, I think you're ready for the Olympics.
Mariana: Oh, I don't think so. I fell down a lot. And I hurt all over.
Shawna: Yeah, but you were doing great! I saw you coming down that hill. You were going really fast.
Mariana: Well, it was fun. It was really fun. Thank you for suggesting this, Cal.
Cal: Hey, this idea was yours. You wanted to go skiing, remember?
Mariana: But I didn't want to fall down!
Cal: Well, everyone falls down. Even Josh!
Jin: Yeah, did you see him today? He fell and wow, it was a big fall!
Mariana: Is he OK?
Shawna: Oh, yeah, he got up and kept skiing. So I don't think he broke anything.
Jin: Yeah, where is Josh, anyway?
Cal: There he is.
Josh: Yeah. Here I am. How is everyone? Mariana, you were great!
Mariana: How are you? I heard that you fell.
Cal: Yeah, what happened? Did you hurt your shoulder?
Josh: Oh, yeah, I hurt my shoulder … but I'm OK. I'm all right.
Jin: Er, the lodge offers Shiatsu massage. I don't know much about Shiatsu, but it might be like acupressure.
Josh: Acupressure? What's that?
Jin: It's like acupuncture, but without the needles. The pressure applied to different parts of your body helps your vital energy – your Chi.
Josh: My what? My vital energy? No, I don't think so.
Jin: I think that it will work. You should try it, Josh. Get a Shiatsu massage. I want to see if it works.
Mariana: Hey, I want to get a Shiatsu massage, too.
Shawna: Yeah, I think it sounds great.
Josh: Oh, that's a lot of hooey.
Jin: I don't think so. It says it relieves stress …
Shawna: Yeah, and it restores energy …
Mariana: And it reduces pain.
Jin: So … why don't you try it?
Josh: Er … no thanks. Just give me a couple of aspirin and a hot tub … Ow!
Jin: Josh. Open your mind!
Josh: No thanks, Jin. I just need a little rest … Aaaah.
Mariana: Let's go over there now.
Jin: Come on.
Josh: OK, OK. I'll try it.

Scene 9C: 48:46 – 49:25

Masseuse: The first stretch hurts.
Josh: Owww! No kidding! Yeah, the first stretch hurts … Aaaaah!
Masseuse: Don't worry, it'll get better.
Josh: Aaaah. Hey, wow. That really does feel better. Yeah. I like this. This is great. Hey, there's a snowboarding competition tomorrow. I'm going to enter!

Unit Nine 9

Pain in the neck

1 Before you watch

▶▶ **Cultural note**

a Read the text and then discuss the questions.

Alternative therapies – including, for example, massage, herbal medicine and homeopathy – are growing fast in the United States. Nearly half of all Americans use an alternative therapy and they spend over $30 billion a year on them. This is more than they spend on visits to hospitals! People are interested in using alternative therapy sometimes because they are not satisfied with conventional medicine, but also because it seems more natural to them. In fact, most American doctors are now able to offer their patients both conventional medicine and alternative therapy.

1 Do you or your family use any alternative therapies?
2 Which forms of alternative therapy are popular in your country?

b Vocabulary

Complete the crossword with the words in the box. Use the clues to help you.

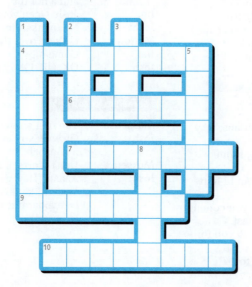

headache   pressure   pain
take   needle   energy   saves
shoulder   massage   relieve

Clues

Across
4 I can't look at the computer any longer. It's giving me a ...
6 The doctor has to put a ... in your arm to give you a shot.
7 I'm sorry your back hurts. Why don't you lie down and I can give you a ...
9 This medicine will help to ... the pain, but you also need to rest your back a lot.
10 Don't put too much ... on my back. It's very sensitive.

Down
1 Part of your body at the top of your arm.
2 Doctor, my leg hurts. Can you give me something to take away the ...?
3 You have to ... two aspirins every four hours.
5 People with a lot of ... never feel tired.
8 A doctor sometimes ... a person's life after an accident.

c Tell your partner about the last time you:

hurt yourself playing sport.
spent a night in the hospital.
had a massage.
missed school or work because you were sick.

read a magazine about health.
had a headache.
had a shot.

Worksheet
Pain in the neck

2 Watch for main ideas

a Watch Unit 9 and choose the correct answer (a, b or c).

1 Shiatsu comes from a) Japan.   b) China.   c) India.
2 Mariana's day was a) terrible.   b) fun.   c) lazy.
3 Josh hurt his a) leg.   b) arm.   c) shoulder.
4 At first Josh thinks Shiatsu is a) frightening.   b) interesting.   c) nonsense.
5 After his massage he feels a) tired.   b) much better.   c) sick.

b What do you think of the idea of a Shiatsu massage?

3 Watch for details

▶▶ Scene 9A

Watch Scene 9A and match the Japanese words with the correct meaning on the right.

1 Shiatsu   a life power
2 Shi   b pressure
3 atsu   c finger
4 Chi   d a Japanese massage

▶▶ Scene 9B

Read these sentences from the scene. Who does the word in bold refer to?
Watch scene 9B again and check (✔) the correct column.

	Mariana	Jin	Josh
1 I think **you**'re ready for the Olympics.	✔		
2 **I** fell down a lot.			
3 **You** were going really fast.			
4 Is **he** OK?			
5 I hurt **my** shoulder.			
6 **I** don't know much about Shiatsu.			
7 **I** want to see if it works.			
8 **I** want to get a Shiatsu massage too.			
9 Open **your** mind.			

▶▶ Scene 9C

a There are six mistakes in the summary. Can you correct them?

At first, the massage feels very good, but the man tells Josh it's going to hurt later. Then it starts to feel worse and Josh thinks it's terrible. He decides to enter a swimming competition the next day.

b Now watch scene 9C again and check your answers.

4 After you watch

Language focus: *should / need to / have to*

a Match the beginnings and endings of the sentences about skiing.

1 You need to   a get on to the mountain early when the snow is best.
2 You should   b go skiing with a group of friends because the nightlife is fun!
3 You have to   c practice the basic techniques over and over again.
                    d buy a ski-pass if you want to go on the mountain.
                    e be very careful because the mountain can be dangerous!
                    f wear goggles to stop the sun getting in your eyes.

b Choose another sport and write six sentences about it, using *You should ..., You need to ...* and *You have to ...* . Read your sentences to the other students and they have to guess the sport.

Unit Ten 10   Teacher's notes

Getting stood up – Summary

When you *get stood up* it means that you had a date with someone, you waited but they didn't come. This is one of the vocabulary items in *Before you watch*. In scene 10A, Josh phones Mariana to check that she's going to Cal's party the next day. He's nervous, but everything seems fine. In scene 10B, Josh nervously waits for her at the party. He's upset because Mariana hasn't arrived. His friends try to reassure him, but it's no good. He eats too much, feels sick and finally leaves just before she arrives, feeling annoyed and upset because he has "gotten stood up." In scene 10C, Mariana arrives and Jin explains what has happened. She phones Josh, explaining that in Venezuela it's normal to turn up late at parties. She asks if he wants to go out for dinner the next day and they agree to meet at seven.

1 Before you watch

▶▶ Cultural note

a ● Ask the students to read the cultural note and look at the pictures as they do so.
● They match the items in the pictures with the words in italics in the text.

> **Answers:** a chicken wings b won tons c steak d hamburgers
> e barbecue

● Then ask them to discuss the questions in pairs or small groups.
b ● Ask the students to read the conversation between two friends and match the underlined words with the expressions underneath. They should be able to do this from the context.
● They can check their answers in pairs before you check as a class.
● Tell them that they will hear these words and phrases in the unit.

> **Answers:** 2 stood me up 3 I doubt it. 4 pick her up
> 5 explanation 6 upset 7 pale

2 Watch for main ideas   49:31 – 56:31

a ● Ask the students to look at the scenes from the video.
● Play the unit through and ask the students to order the scenes according to when they appear.

> **Answers:** 1C 2B 3E 4A 5D

b ● Then ask the students to discuss what is happening and how Josh feels in each one.
c ● Ask the students to try to answer the questions. Play the unit through again if necessary, though the students should be able to answer the questions from memory as they are quite general.
● Check their answers.

> **Answers:** 1 To ask if she is going to Cal's party. 2 No, because Mariana isn't there. 3 He asks if they've seen her. 4 To apologize and explain why she was late.

◀◀ Rewind the video to 10A 49:47 in preparation for **Watch for details**.

3 Watch for details   Scene 10A: 49:47 – 51:14

a ● Ask the students to read through the statements.
● Make sure they understand that the statements may be said by Mariana, Josh or by both of them.
● Play the scene again for the students to check (✔) the chart.
● Play it a second time if necessary, then check their answers.

> **Answers:**
>
> | | | Mariana | Josh |
> |---|--------------------|---------|------|
> | 1 | It was really fun. | | ✔ |
> | 2 | I feel great. | | ✔ |
> | 3 | He invited me. | ✔ | ✔ |
> | 4 | I'm going. | ✔ | ✔ |
> | 5 | That's great. | ✔ | ✔ |
> | 6 | I'll see you there.| ✔ | ✔ |
> | 7 | five o'clock | ✔ | |
> | 8 | Tomorrow | ✔ | ✔ |

b ● Ask the students why Mariana and Josh repeat what each other says so much. Possible reasons: they're nervous / they can't think of anything to say / they want to make sure of things.

▶▶ Scene 10B: 51:18 – 54:44

a ● Pre-teach any new vocabulary as necessary, e.g. *be supposed to* (something a person should do but often doesn't), *ginger tea* (tea made from the ginger root).
● Tell the students to look at the times in the chart and that they have to match the events with the times.
● Have the students watch the scene again and match the times and events.
● Check their answers.

> **Answers:** 1b 2a 3d 4e 5c

b ● Ask the students to match the people with what they said.
● Play the scene again for them to check their answers.

> **Answers:** a Cal b Sara c Shawna d Jin

▶▶ Scene 10C: 54:47 – 56:31

● Ask the students if they can remember why Mariana was late (because it's normal in Venezuela to go to parties very late).
● Ask the students to read the questions. Pre-teach any new vocabulary as necessary, e.g. *expect someone to do something* (to believe that a person will do something), *miss* (here: arriving after he had left).
● Play the scene again for the students to make notes of the answers.
● They write their answers. Make sure they realize they should write only short answers.
● Check their answers. Play the scene again if necessary.

> **Answers:** 1 Upset 2 At five or five-thirty 3 Very late
> 4 She asks if he wants to go out for dinner. 5 Yes, they make sure!

4 After you watch

Language focus: present perfect
- This practices language from pages 88 and 89 of the Student's Book.
- Have the students discuss in pairs or small groups. They could ask about other events and also discuss if they think people from other countries have different customs.

5 Communication activity

Turn to page 62 for the *Party game* activity.

Video Script COUNTER 49:31–56:31

Scene 10A: 49:47 – 51:14

Mariana:	Hello.
Josh:	Uh … so … hi, Mariana.
Mariana:	Hi, Josh. How are you?
Josh:	Oh, I'm fine. I had a great time skiing. It was really fun.
Mariana:	Yeah, it was really fun. It's so hard to go back to work … So … are you feeling better?
Josh:	Oh, yeah, yeah. I feel great. That massage really … uh, so, I was wondering … er … are you going to Cal's party tomorrow?
Mariana:	Oh, yes. Sure. He invited me. I'm going.
Josh:	Oh, that's great. Because, you know. I mean he invited me, too, so … I'm going too.
Mariana:	Oh, great. That's great.
Josh:	So … Uh … I'll see you there?
Mariana:	Oh, yes. I'll see you there.
Josh:	OK. So, good. You know the party starts at five?
Mariana:	Right. It starts at five o'clock, yeah.
Josh:	Okay, great. Then I'll see you tomorrow.
Mariana:	Right. Tomorrow at Cal's. And uh, thanks for calling.
Josh:	Yes!
Mariana:	All right.

Scene 10B: 51:18 – 54:44

Cal:	Hey, you guys. Have you tried these chicken wings? Shawna made them. They're really spicy …
Sara:	These are great. They're not too spicy.
Shawna:	Thank you.
Sara:	This is a nice place. I love the yard.
Josh:	Hey, Sara, have you seen Mariana?
Sara:	Uh, no. Well, I saw her at home. She said she was coming. She said she'd be here later.
Josh:	Oh, hey, Cal.
Cal:	Hey …
Josh:	She sure is late …
Cal:	Oh, she's coming. She's coming. Hey, look at that plate. You must have eaten … about three pounds of those wings.
Josh:	Oh, I did. I ate them all!
Shawna:	Hey, Josh. Jin made some won tons. Have you tried them?
Sara:	You should try them, Josh. They're hot!
Josh:	Uh … won tons? Not now.
Sara:	Oh come on, they're really good.
Josh:	Maybe just one. Oh, these are good. Thanks.
Shawna:	Josh … Are you okay?
Josh:	Well, it's just … Mariana was supposed to meet me here. She *knew* what time it started. It's really late.
Sara:	Maybe … I don't know, maybe she got lost.
Josh:	Thanks, but, well … I don't really think that she got lost.
Shawna:	Oh, but … You know, I'm sure there's an explanation. Hey, do you want to call her? There's a phone in the …
Josh:	No, thanks, Shawna. It's OK.
Jin:	Hey, Josh.
Josh:	Hey, Jin. Those won tons you made were great.
Jin:	Oh, thanks. I think you look a little pale. Are you feeling all right?
Josh:	Oh, yeah, I'm fine. Man, I waited for her for over an hour and a half and she didn't come. She said she was going to. I can't believe it!
Jin:	I don't know … I'm sorry, maybe … maybe something happened.
Josh:	Yeah, but I doubt it.
Jin:	Mariana wouldn't do that. She's not like that.
Josh:	Look, I'm not feeling too well. I think I ate too much … I'm out of here …
Jin:	OK, I'll see you later. Try some ginger tea, there's some in the kitchen. It will help you out with your stomach.
Josh:	Ginger tea, huh. OK Jin. I'll try it.

Scene 10C: 54:47 – 56:31

Mariana:	Hey, Jin. How's it going?
Jin:	Mariana!
Mariana:	Hey, have you seen Josh?
Jin:	Yes, he just left. I think he was kind of upset.
Mariana:	Upset?
Jin:	Yeah. I think he thought that you weren't coming.
Mariana:	But why? I don't understand.
Jin:	The party started at 5:00. So he was expecting to meet you here at about 5:30. 6:00 at the latest.
Mariana:	5:30? Really? Are … are you sure?
Jin:	Uh, I'm pretty sure that's what he thought …
Mariana:	Oh no. In Venezuela, people usually arrive at parties really late.
Jin:	Oh, you see it's different here. If a party starts at 5:00, most people go at about 5:30. Josh thought you'd be here by that time.
Mariana:	I'm so sorry. I really … When I got here, I saw Jin and he told me that you waited for me a long time.
Josh:	Yeah, I did wait for a while.
Mariana:	You see … in Venezuela, it's so different. Most people don't go to parties until late … and I just … I guess I thought it was the same here …
Josh:	I never knew that. About people going late …
Mariana:	Er, maybe we can … I don't know … get together tomorrow … would you like to go to dinner?
Josh:	Dinner? Uh … sure. I'll pick you up at … I'll pick you up at 7:00.
Mariana:	Seven o'clock. OK. Does that mean seven o'clock?
Josh:	Yes, that means seven o'clock.
Mariana:	Okay, goodnight, Josh.
Josh:	Goodnight, Mariana. See you tomorrow.

45

Unit Ten 10

Getting stood up

1 Before you watch

▶▶ **Cultural note**

a **Read the text and then discuss the questions.**

Americans like to invite friends to their house for a party. If it's good weather, they love to have a *barbecue* in the back yard and everyone brings some food or drink. Traditionally, they put *steak* or *hamburgers* on the barbecue but it's also common to have Mexican or Chinese food too – like spicy *chicken wings* or *won tons*. Barbecues often start in the afternoon and friends eat, drink and talk until the evening.

a

b

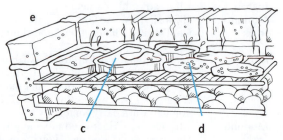

1 Match the words in *italics* in the cultural note with the correct picture.
2 Do you have barbecues? How often?
3 What time do they usually start and finish?
4 Do people to bring food and drink with them?

b **Read this conversation between two friends and write the underlined words next to the similar expressions below.**

Richard: What's the problem, Paul? You look <u>pale</u>.
Paul: I think I ate and drank too much this evening.
Richard: Didn't you have <u>a date</u> with Amanda tonight?
Paul: Yes, that was the problem. She <u>stood me up</u>.
Richard: No, really? There must be a simple <u>explanation</u>.
Paul: <u>I doubt it</u>. I waited for an hour at the restaurant. That's why I ate so much!
Richard: But she was waiting for you to <u>pick her up</u> at her house.
Paul: Really? Oh no!
Richard: I think you should call her. She'll be <u>upset</u>!

1 a romantic meeting   <u>a date</u>
2 didn't arrive for a meeting _____
3 I don't believe it _____
4 collect someone by car _____
5 a reason why something happened _____
6 unhappy _____
7 white-faced and ill _____

2 Watch for main ideas

a **Watch Unit 10 and put the pictures below in the order you see them in the video.**

A   B   C   D   E

_____   _____   _____   _____   _____

Worksheet 10
Getting stood up

b How do you think Josh is feeling in these scenes?

c Can you answer these questions?

1 Why does Josh phone Mariana?
2 Is Josh happy at the party?
3 What does he ask his friends at the party?
4 Why does Mariana phone Josh?

3 Watch for details

▶▶ Scene 10A

a Watch scene 10A again. Who says what? Check (✔) Mariana, Josh or both.

		Mariana	Josh			Mariana	Josh
1	It was really fun.	✔	✔	5	That's great.		
2	I feel great.			6	I'll see you there.		
3	He invited me.			7	five o'clock		
4	I'm going.			8	Tomorrow.		

b Why do you think they repeat things so much?

▶▶ Scene 10B

a Watch scene 10B again and match each event with the correct time.

 1   2   3   4   5

a Josh is drinking a beer.
b Cal's party starts.
c Josh leaves the party.
d Josh starts eating chicken wings.
e Josh starts eating won tons.

b All of Josh's friends try to stop him worrying about Mariana. Who says what?

a She's coming. She's coming.   Sara
b Maybe she got lost.   Jin
c I'm sure there's an explanation. Shawna
d Maybe something happened.   Cal

▶▶ Scene 10C

Watch scene 10C again and then write short answers to the questions.

1 How did Josh feel when he left the party?
2 What time did Josh expect Mariana to arrive at the party?
3 When do people in Venezuela normally arrive at parties?
4 How does she make up for missing him at the party?
5 Are they sure what time they're going to meet tomorrow?

4 After you watch

Language focus: present perfect

Which of the things in the box have you arrived late for? How often? Answer for each one.

e.g. *I have often arrived late for a date. I have never arrived late for an exam. I have arrived late for an international flight once.*

a date   an exam   a party   a movie   a wedding   school   an international flight   work

Unit Eleven 11

Teacher's notes

A promotion — Summary

This unit is mainly about Shawna's dissatisfaction at work. In scene 11A, Joan announces that they've won the Fruity Fruit account, but they all have a lot more work to do. She gives Luis, Shawna and Mariana a list of tasks to do as soon as possible. In scene 11B, Shawna complains to Al that she's now doing a producer's job but not earning a producer's salary. Al encourages her to ask Joan for a raise. In scene 11C, Shawna expresses her frustration to Joan. Joan offers to train Shawna as a producer when the Fruity Fruit project is finished, but says she can't give her a raise. Shawna threatens to leave, and after the meeting talks to Al again and is afraid she'll have to look for another job.

1 Before you watch

▶▶ **Cultural note**

a
- Introduce the topic by saying that Shawna is having problems at work because she feels she's doing a lot of work and not getting enough money. Ask if the students have any ideas why.
- Pre-teach any new vocabulary as necessary, e.g. *opportunities* (chances).
- Have them read the note and discuss the questions. The topic may be rather controversial, so it may be best not to discuss it for too long.
- Ask if they are surprised by the information. Note that Shawna is a black woman – so perhaps that contributes to her dissatisfaction at work. Do they agree?

b
- Tell the students that this exercise will help them with some of the work-related vocabulary on the video.
- Have the students match the words and phrases with the definitions, using dictionaries if necessary.
- Have them check in pairs before you check the answers with the whole group.

Answers: 1f 2h 3b 4g 5c 6a 7e 8d

c
- These questions should allow the students to practice some of the new vocabulary and prepare them for some of the themes in the video.
- Have the students discuss the questions in pairs or small groups.
- If your students have not worked, have them discuss what they think normally happens.
- You could ask some students to say their ideas to the rest of the class.
- Ideas for number 1 may include the use of focus groups and surveys, questionnaires sent to households, people approaching you in the street. For number 4, they may include qualifications, performance or seniority.

2 Watch for main ideas   56:37 – 61:30

- Pre-teach any new vocabulary as necessary, e.g. *salary* (money you earn at work), *producer* (the person responsible for bringing everything together on a film, TV ad, etc.), *satisfied* (quite happy), *optimistic* (sure that the future will be good).

- Play the video. The students watch and choose the correct answer.
- Have them check their answers in pairs before you check with the whole group.

Answers: 1c 2b 3a 4c 5b

◀◀ Rewind the video to 11A 56:53 in preparation for **Watch for details**.

3 Watch for details   Scene 11A: 56:53 – 57:48

- Have the students watch the video and draw a line from each person to the tasks they have to do.
- The information is quite detailed but some of it is on the flipchart in the background of the scene, which should help.
- Have the students compare with their partners before you check with the whole group.

Answers: Mariana 4; Luis 1, 5; Shawna 2, 3, 6, 7

▶▶ **Scene 11B: 57:52 – 59:20**

a
- Have the students read the sentences before watching. Pre-teach any new vocabulary as necessary, e.g. *mad* (annoyed, angry).
- As they watch, they write 1-5 next to the sentences in the order of the events.

Answers: a3 b5 c2 d1 e4

b
- The students now use the sentences and anything else they can remember to make a short summary. Let them practice in pairs and then ask two or three pairs to read their summary aloud.

▶▶ **Scene 11C: 59:22 – 61:30**

- Have the students read the statements before watching.
- Pre-teach any new vocabulary as necessary, e.g. *responsibility* (taking on a lot of duties), *work your way up* (gradually train and take on more responsibilities).
- As they watch, mark T or F next to the statements.
- After you have checked their answers, ask the students to correct the false statements if they can.

Answers: 1T 2T 3F (She's doing some of a producer's job.) 4F (She thinks she'll be a good producer.) 5T 6T 7F (She says she will look for another job.) 8T

4 After you watch

Language focus: *do* and *make*
- This exercise gives the students extra practice of expressions with *do* and *make*.
- Have the students complete the questions. (They could look at page 97 of their Student's Books or at a dictionary for help with the answers.)
- Check their answers.

Answers: do, make, make, do, do, make, do, make, do

- In pairs, have the students ask each other the questions.
- Encourage them to ask follow-up questions, with *why* and *when*, etc.

5 Communication activity

Turn to page 62 for the *Asking for a raise* activity.

Video Script COUNTER 56:37–61:30 ▶▶▶

Scene 11A: 56:53 – 57:48

Joan:	OK, good news – we got the Fruity Fruit account!
Mariana:	All right!
Luis:	That's great.
Shawna:	I knew we could do it.
Joan:	Good work, people. But now the real work begins. So let's review this task list. Mariana, they liked your concept, but they want to know it's going to work. So you're going to set up test focus groups in the Boston area. OK, Luis, make all the graphic changes they asked for. They liked that T-shirt concept, so make a T-shirt. OK, Shawna, make a new production schedule – send it to the client. Set up a casting session. We need the right actors for these ads! OK, we need a lot more market research … on ages, what they like, you know what to do. Write a report. OK, and basically that's all for this morning. All right.
Shawna:	Well, we really must have wowed them!

Scene 11B: 57:52 – 59:20

Al:	Hey, what's wrong, Shawna?
Shawna:	Me? Oh, nothing. Nothing's wrong.
Al:	Nothing, huh? Then why do you look so mad?
Shawna:	What …
Al:	I mean, you look pretty mad.
Shawna:	Do I look mad? Well, I guess I am pretty mad.
Al:	Why? What's the matter? Tell Al all about it.
Shawna:	Oh, Al. It's Joan! Look at my job description. Office manager. But what am I doing? I'm creating production schedules … I'm setting up casting sessions … doing market research … writing reports … I'm doing lots of things that aren't in my job description.
Al:	Well, you're right, it's not an office manager's job. That's a producer's job.
Shawna:	Well, I'm certainly not making a producer's salary! I'm making much, much less. I should be getting paid a lot more.
Al:	Shawna. Do you think Joan's going to come in here right now and say, "Shawna, honey, you are so great, you are so fantastic! Please, let me give you more money!"
Shawna:	No, of course not!
Al:	No. Joan will only give you more money if you ask for it.
Shawna:	Yeah, I know. You're right.
Al:	Well then what are you waiting for? Go ask her.
Shawna:	Well …
Al:	Go in there and ask her for more money. If you want something, you have to go for it. Go, girl!
Shawna:	Jeez, Al. You sound just like my mother!
Al:	That's the first time anybody has ever told me *that*!

Scene 11C: 59:22 – 61:30

Joan:	Yes, you wanted to talk to me?
Shawna:	Yes. I wanted to talk to you about my job.
Joan:	You're doing a great job, Shawna, a great job. You've taken on a lot of responsibility.
Shawna:	Oh, well. I'm glad you see it that way, Joan. Because I've realized I'm not doing the job of an office manager any more.
Joan:	Oh?
Shawna:	No, I'm doing what a producer does.
Joan:	You're doing *some* of what a producer does, but you're not doing everything … Is that what you'd like to do? Produce?
Shawna:	Yes. I'd like to do that … but what I really want …
Joan:	Because I think you'd be good at it. You'd be a good producer.
Shawna:	Oh, well, thank you. I …
Joan:	Well, here's what you can do. You can work your way up. You can train with the producer … the best we have … then, in like six months … we'll see. But I'm sure you'll do well …
Shawna:	Yes, Joan. I do want to be a producer. And I'll work hard for it …
Joan:	Good. Good. You know what? But first we need to finish this Fruity Fruit job. We've got the account, but we have a lot of work to do. Then you can train with the producer.
Shawna:	Fine, but I'm still doing a lot of extra work … I'm working lots of extra hours … I'm doing a lot more work than what an office manager does … So I think I should get more money …
Joan:	I know you're working hard, we all are working hard. I just can't give you a raise right now.
Shawna:	Joan, I've worked really hard since I started here, and I've done so much extra work. I really want a raise or …
Joan:	Or what, Shawna?
Shawna:	Or … I'll have to leave. I'll have to look for another job.
Joan:	Well … I certainly would hate to lose you.
Al:	Well, what happened?
Shawna:	I don't know. I think I'm going to have to look for another job!
Al:	Oh no!

49

Unit Eleven **11**

A promotion

1 Before you watch

▸▸ **Cultural note**

a Read the text and then discuss the questions.

The United States may be the land of opportunity, but it seems that some people have to fight harder for their opportunities than others. There are four female office workers for every man, but two men for every woman in management jobs. And not even one in twenty American managers is a black or Hispanic woman.

1 Is the situation similar in your country?
2 How fast do you think things are changing?
3 Do you think the situation should change?

b Match the words and phrases on the left with their definitions.

1	a promotion	a	the document that tells you what you have to do at work
2	a casting session	b	a group of ordinary people talking about what they like and dislike
3	a focus group	c	finding out about what people want
4	a raise	d	organize
5	market research	e	a piece of work that you have to do
6	a job description	f	getting a better position in your company
7	a task	g	more money for your work
8	set up	h	a meeting to choose actors or models

c Unit 11 is about the world of work. Discuss these questions.

1 What different methods of market research are there?
2 Have you ever asked your boss for a raise?
3 What is your job description? Do you often have to do work that is not in your job description?
4 How do people normally get promotion where you work?
5 Do you ever have to do tasks that you dislike?

2 Watch for main ideas

Watch Unit 11 and choose the correct answer (a, b or c).

1 Joan tells the team that a) they've worked too hard.   b) they're working too hard.
c) they have a lot of work to do.

2 Shawna is mad because a) she can't do all the things Joan wants her to do.
b) she thinks her salary should be higher. c) she wants to be a producer.

3 Al thinks a) Shawna is doing a producer's job.   b) Shawna should leave the company.
c) Joan is going to offer Shawna more money.

4 Joan thinks that Shawna a) is a good producer.   b) should look for another job.
c) has to finish the project before her training starts.

5 When Shawna leaves Joan's office, she feels a) satisfied.   b) worried.   c) optimistic.

PHOTOCOPIABLE

50   Copyright © Macmillan Publishers Limited 2002.

Worksheet
A promotion

3 Watch for details

▶▶ Scene 11A

Watch scene 11A again and match the people with the correct sentences.

... has to
1 make a T-shirt
2 do more market research
3 make a new production schedule
4 set up focus groups
5 make graphic changes
6 write a report
7 set up a casting session

▶▶ Scene 11B

a Watch scene 11B and put these sentences in the order you hear them.

a Shawna says she wants a higher salary.	
b Shawna says Al sounds like her mother.	
c Shawna says she's pretty mad.	
d Al asks Shawna what's wrong.	
e Al says Shawna should ask Joan for more money.	

b Use the sentences to make a short summary of the scene.

▶▶ Scene 11C

Watch scene 11C again. Mark each statement T (True) or F (False).

1 Shawna has made an appointment to see Joan.   T ☐   F ☐
2 Joan is very happy with Shawna's work.   T ☐   F ☐
3 Joan agrees that Shawna is doing a producer's job.   T ☐   F ☐
4 Joan thinks Shawna is a good producer.   T ☐   F ☐
5 Shawna thinks she should get more money.   T ☐   F ☐
6 Joan can't give Shawna more money.   T ☐   F ☐
7 Shawna tells Joan she's looking for another job.   T ☐   F ☐
8 Al is unhappy with the result of Shawna's meeting.   T ☐   F ☐

4 After you watch

Language focus: *do* and *make*

Complete the questions with *do* or *make*. Then ask your partner about their job.

How often do you …

_____ a lot of extra work?   _____ extra money because your work was good?
_____ a mess in your office?   _____ something very different at work?
_____ some changes to your office?   _____ plans for the future?
_____ some exercise before work?   _____ two jobs at the same time?
_____ some research about other jobs?

Unit Twelve 12 — Teacher's notes

Predicting the future – Summary

In this unit Shawna and her friends visit Jennifer's shop, where they hope to get some predictions about Shawna's future. In scene 12A, Shawna returns home worried about losing her job and Sara suggests going to Jennifer's bookshop. In scene 12B, the friends go to Jennifer's bookshop and Jin finds a book on Chinese astrology. He asks the others when they were born and tells them which animal they are and what characteristics they have. Shawna asks him if he thinks she'll get a raise and he says she will – if not now, then soon. In scene 12C, Joan gives Shawna a raise but tells her she has to earn it. She promises she will.

1 Before you watch

▶▶ **Cultural note**

a ● Pre-teach any new vocabulary as necessary, e.g. *astrology* (predicting the future by date of birth), *zodiac* (the year divided into the twelve signs which influence our characteristics according to our date of birth, e.g. if you were born on 15th June, you are a Gemini; if you were born on 4th February, you are an Aquarius).
● Have the students read the note.
● Ask the students to look at the Chinese horoscope.
● Have the students work in pairs to name the animals they know.
● They can then compare with other pairs and discuss as a class to complete the rest.
● Explain that the horoscope goes in 12-year cycles, so the dragon (A) would be every 12 years, i.e. 1952, 1964, 1976, 1988.
● Note that some Chinese horoscopes use the sheep (or lamb) and others use the goat.

Answers: A dragon, B snake, C horse, D sheep, E monkey, F dog, G rooster, H pig, I rat, J ox, K tiger, L rabbit

● Don't worry if the students don't understand all the adjectives, as they are the focus of the next exercise.
● Have the students discuss the questions in small groups.
● Be sensitive and emphasize that it is just for fun, as some students may have very negative opinions about this kind of thing.
b ● Have the students work in pairs to match the adjectives and definitions.
● Help them with the pronunciation of the adjectives if necessary.

Answers: 1d 2a 3h 4e 5f 6g 7i 8b 9c

2 Watch for main ideas   61:39 – 67:52

● Read the rubric and have the students decide which five things might happen in the unit.
● Play Unit 12 through for them to check their answers before you check as a class.

Answers: 1, 3, 5, 6, 7

◀◀ Rewind the video to 12A 61:54 in preparation for **Watch for details**.

3 Watch for details   Scene 12A: 61:54 – 62:32

● Pre-teach any new vocabulary as necessary, e.g. *quit* (leave a place / job).
● Have the students look at the sentences first and ask them to think carefully about the situation.
● They then circle the correct verb forms.
● Play scene 12A again for them to check.

Answers: 1 We're just going to go 2 I'll quit 3 You're going to quit? 4 what's going to happen. 5 what's going to happen 6 It'll be

▶▶ **Scene 12B: 62:35 – 67:21**

● Explain what the students have to do and tell them that more than one person has the same animal.
● Pre-teach any new vocabulary as necessary, e.g. *qualities* (characteristics), *ups and downs in life* (good and bad times).
● The students watch scene 12B again and draw lines from the people to the relevant animals.
● Check their answers.

Answers: Jennifer – dragon, Cal – horse, Sara – horse, Josh – horse, Luis – sheep, Jin – monkey, Mariana – snake, Shawna – snake

▶▶ **Scene 12C: 67:24 – 67:52**

● Have the students read the questions and then watch the scene.
● There's no need for them to write – the scene is short.
● Have them check with their partners before you check the answers with the whole group.

Answers: 1 Yes. 2 Not very – it's a small raise.
3 happy / grateful / relieved

4 After you watch

Language focus: connectors
● This exercise gives the students more practice of the connectors on page 111 of the Student's Book.
● **Note** that *However* and *but* are equivalent, but the punctuation makes a difference: ask the students to look at the examples in the Student's Book and notice that *However* begins a new sentence.

Answers: 1 However 2 because 3 but 4 However 5 so 6 so

Discussion
● Have the students discuss their predictions in pairs.
● Ask them to give reasons for their predictions.
● Discuss them as a class and try to come to a consensus.

5 Communication activity

Turn to page 62 for the *Skyline video quiz* activity.

52

Video Script

COUNTER 61:39–67:52

Scene 12A: 61:54 – 62:32

Cal:	Hey, we were waiting for you.
Shawna:	Hey.
Cal:	We're just going to go out to dinner. Come on! Let's go.
Shawna:	Oh, I don't know. I told Joan today that I really want a raise or … I'll quit.
Sara:	You're going to quit?
Shawna:	Well, I don't want to but … oh now I'm so nervous … I don't know what's going to happen … I just don't think I could eat dinner.
Sara:	Hey, I have an idea. Let's go to Jennifer's shop! She has all kinds of ways to tell the future! Let's find out what's going to happen to Shawna. Come on! It'll be fun.
Shawna:	Fun for you guys!

Scene 12B: 62:35 – 67:21

Josh:	OK we're walking … we're walking up … and here we are at the world famous Unicorn Books.
Mariana:	Wow! This looks like fun.
Josh:	Hey.
Jennifer:	Hi, it's so good to see you guys here. What's up? I was just about to close the shop.
Josh:	We need to know Shawna's future.
Jin:	Hey, Chinese astrology!
Jennifer:	Oh, yes. I don't know very much about horoscopes.
Jin:	I do.
Sara:	Yeah?
Josh:	Come on, Shawna. Let's go.
Jin:	OK, write down your birthdays – month, day, year. The Chinese horoscope is based upon the year that you were born. Each year is ruled by a different animal. And the people born in that year share the same qualities as that animal.
Mariana:	Animal qualities! I don't know …
Jin:	You see, it's a 12-year cycle, starting with the rat. Following the rat, is the ox, the tiger, the rabbit, the dragon, the snake, the horse, the sheep, the monkey, the rooster, the dog, the pig and back to the rat. Er … let's see, Jennifer, you were born in the year of the dragon …
Jennifer:	What does that mean?
Jin:	It means that you are very intellectual and you like complicated situations. You will have many ups and downs in your life. And you will have difficult times, but you will find happiness.
Josh:	Are dragons perfect?
Jin:	No, sometimes they are too stubborn to change their opinions.
Cal:	So, what am I?
Jin:	Let's see. Cal, wow. We have a lot of horses here. You and Sara and Josh are all horses.
Cal:	Horse huh? It sounds good. I like that.
Josh:	Yeah, I like being a horse. I didn't want to be a rabbit.
Cal:	Yeah, or a rat.
Sara:	So, tell us about horses.
Jin:	OK. Horses are free-spirited. And you know, you *don't* like to follow the rules. You are very quick thinkers. And you are very intelligent.
Josh:	Hey, intelligent …
Cal:	Yeah, that's definitely us.
Jin:	Horses have a great sense of humor. And you like to make people laugh, your humor will get you through difficult times in your life. Horses fall in love very easily though! And when they fall in love, they get very distracted … they can't even function!
Sara:	So … uh … who should a horse marry?
Jin:	Ideally, a horse should ideally marry a sheep, a dog or a tiger.
Sara:	So, what's Luis?
Jin:	Luis I think is a sheep. Sheep are very artistic and elegant. Very creative. Luis will always want beauty and comfort in his life. A sheep can be shy as well too.
Mariana:	Shy?
Jin:	Umm, shy, uh … timid …
Sara:	What are you, Jin?
Jin:	Me? I am a monkey.
Josh:	So does that mean you're funny?
Jin:	Er, yes, we have a good sense of humor … we like to play jokes on people, and there is always romance in our life. But that's neither here nor there. Let's see … There are two snakes. Mariana and Shawna.
Shawna:	I'm a snake! Oh no.
Mariana:	A snake? Is that bad?
Cal:	Oooh, snakes, that's bad!
Shawna:	Hey!
Jin:	You all have Western ideas about snakes … and rabbits and rats but in Eastern culture, we have much different ideas about those animals. A snake-year woman is considered the *most* beautiful woman. It is a great compliment to tell a woman that she has the beauty of a snake-year woman.
Shawna:	Great beauty, of course! Right, Mariana?
Josh:	Oh, you're just saying that so they'll be happy!
Mariana:	Josh! You don't think we're beautiful?
Josh:	Well, I mean you are *both* beautiful, but … uh … so are Sara and Jennifer!
Jin:	Snakes are very wise and determined. Snakes are very competitive and they always want to win.
Cal:	Oh, now that's definitely true! You always want to *win*!
Shawna:	I do not.
Cal:	Yes, you do.
Shawna:	Do not.
Cal:	Do too!
Mariana:	So … who should a snake marry?
Jin:	Uh … for you an ox or a rooster is best … but marrying a horse is also good.
Shawna:	But, what about me and my job? Does my horoscope say if I'll get my raise?
Jin:	Well, it says you like to win … and so I think that if you don't get it now, you will get it soon.
Shawna:	If not now, soon?
Jin:	Just be patient!
Shawna:	Oh, all right … let's just go out to dinner!

Scene 12C: 67:24 – 67:52

Shawna:	Joan, you wanted to see me?
Joan:	Oh yes Shawna, I've thought about our conversation.
Shawna:	Yes?
Joan:	I've worked really hard to do this, but I will be able to give you a small raise.
Shawna:	Thank you, Joan. Thank you so much.
Joan:	You're welcome. Now earn it.
Shawna:	I will, I promise!

Unit Twelve 12

Predicting the future

1 Before you watch

▶▶ **Cultural note**

a Read the text and then answer the questions.

Astrology first became popular in the United States in the 1930s, when many newspapers and magazines started to include horoscopes. Most people know the Western type of astrology, which looks at the twelve signs of the zodiac for each year. Chinese astrology is different from Western astrology as the signs are animals and each animal represents a number of different years, e.g. if you were born in 1964, 1976 or 1988, you are a dragon and that means you are intellectual and stubborn. This is the Chinese horoscope:

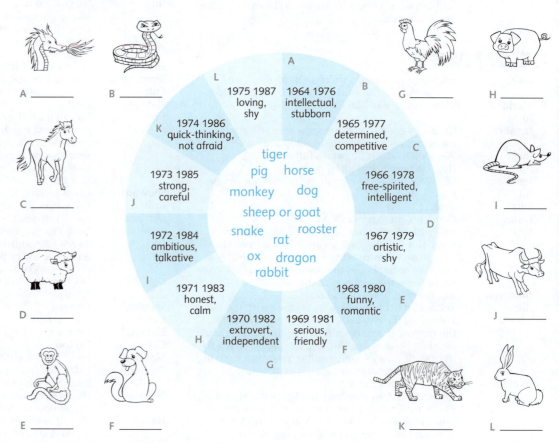

1 Write the names of the animals under the pictures.
2 Which animals are you and members of your family? Do you and your family have the qualities of "your" animals?

b Match the adjectives and definitions.

1 stubborn   a you have a lot of good ideas and imagination
2 creative   b you decide on something, then do it until you succeed
3 intellectual   c you're different from other people and do things your way
4 artistic   d you don't like to change your mind or do things other people tell you to do
5 elegant   e you're good at making things like paintings
6 shy   f you have a good and attractive style
7 wise   g you're nervous about meeting new people and being in public
8 determined   h you like to think deeply about things
9 free-spirited   i you have experience and make good decisions

54

Worksheet
Predicting the future

2 Watch for main ideas

a Remember that Shawna asked Joan for a raise in Unit 11. This unit is called "Predicting the future." Which of these events do you think will happen in this unit? Check (✔) five sentences.

1 Shawna arrives home from work and tells her friends that she might quit. ☐
2 They all go out for a pizza. ☐
3 They go to Jennifer's shop to find out their horoscopes. ☐
4 Jin predicts the future for all of his friends. ☐
5 Cal and Josh are happy about their horoscopes. ☐
6 Jin tells Shawna that she will get a raise in the future. ☐
7 Joan gives Shawna good news and Shawna promises to work hard. ☐
8 Joan gives Shawna bad news and Shawna decides to quit. ☐

b Now watch Unit 12 and check your answers.

3 Watch for details

▶▶ Scene 12A

a Circle the correct verb forms.

1 **Cal:** *We're just going to go / We'll just go* out to dinner.
2 **Shawna:** I told Joan today that I really want a raise or *I quit / I'll quit*.
3 **Sara:** *You quit? / You're going to quit?*
4 **Shawna:** I don't know *what's happening / what's going to happen*.
5 **Sara:** Let's find out *what's happening / what's going to happen* to Shawna.
6 **Sara:** Come on! *It'll be / it's going to be* fun.

b Now watch scene 12A again and check your answers.

▶▶ Scene 12B

Watch scene 12B again and match the person to their animal in the Chinese horoscope.

Jennifer   Cal   Sara   Josh   Luis   Jin   Mariana   Shawna

snake   horse   monkey   dragon   sheep

▶▶ Scene 12C
1 Was Jin's prediction correct?   2 How generous is Joan?   3 How does Shawna feel?

4 After you watch

Language focus: connectors
Complete these sentences with *but, however, so* **or** *because*.

1 Jin is a serious biology student. _____ , he's also interested in astrology.
2 Mariana and Shawna should be happy _____ they were born in the year of the snake.
3 Cal, Sara and Josh are all horses, _____ they're very different people!
4 In the West, people have a bad opinion about rats and snakes. _____ , in the East, people have different ideas about them.
5 Shawna wants to know what's going to happen _____ she asks Jin if he can help.
6 Joan doesn't want to lose Shawna, _____ she gives her a raise.

Discussion
What are your predictions for the people in the video?

Are Josh and Mariana going to get together? Is Jin going to pass his exams? Is Jennifer going to find someone from the video dating agency? Is Shawna going to become a producer?

Copyright © Macmillan Publishers Limited 2002.

Communication activities

Teacher's notes

Activity 1

▶▶ **Saying it without words – a mime game**
- Tell the students to imagine that they are in the United States and have to ask a question. The problem is that the other person can't hear them – it's very noisy – so they have to "say it without words" – in other words using mime.
- Have them read through the cards and check any unfamiliar vocabulary with you or in a dictionary.
- Demonstrate the activity for them. Take one card and mime the question encouraging the students to guess **exactly** the words on the card.
- Then have a student come out and mime out another question for the class to guess. The student who successfully guesses the question can nominate another student to do the next card.
- If you wish, you could have the students continue in a whole class activity or have them play the game in smaller groups.

Activity 2

▶▶ **Designing your new office – a pairwork activity**
- Make a copy of the instructions and an office plan for each student. If possible, enlarge the office plan. If not, you could have the students draw a larger version of the plan, to scale.
- Explain to the students what they have to do – first place all the items of furniture and equipment in the office as they would like them, then compare and negotiate with their partner to arrive at an agreed design.
- Have the students complete their plan by drawing in pictures of the furniture where they think it should go (preferably using a pencil). Do a brief demonstration using the board.
- When they have finished their plan, tell the students that they now have to agree with their partner about the design of the office. So they sit together with their partner and compare their ideas until they produce a plan they can agree on.
- Have some of the pairs present their final plan to the rest of the class, using the board.
- If you prefer, the students could work in pairs on their first office plan and then in groups of four on the final version. You could also tell the students not to show their plan to their new partner if you wish them to practice prepositions of place. Their new partner could try to copy their plan by listening to a description.

Activity 3

▶▶ **What's the best way of …? – a discussion**
- Have your students work in groups of three.
- Give each student in each group a letter (A, B or C).
- Tell them that Student A thinks the Internet is best for everything, Student B thinks the telephone is best for everything and Student C thinks videos or CDs are best for everything.
- Copy and cut up enough sets of activities for each group, and give each group a set of cards face down on the table. Do a demonstration with one group so that all the other groups know what to do and what not to do.
- Student A turns over a card – for example "learning English" and has to say why it's best to do this on the Internet.
- The others disagree and say why the telephone or video is best.
- The one who gives the best reason(s) why their way is best keeps the card. The idea is to get the most cards.
- If you have different numbers of students, have some pairs of student A and student B.
- Monitor the activity, encouraging the students to continue to use English, helping with vocabulary as necessary, but not getting too involved, as your presence may interfere with the communication that is going on.

Worksheet

▶▶ **Activity 1: Saying it without words**

Can I pay by credit card?	Where is the zoo?	Can I play basketball near here?	Can you help me with these bags?	Are you from Brazil?
What time is the last bus?	Can I sit here, please?	Do you have a pen?	Is this the airport bus?	Is there a supermarket near here?
Is there a public phone near here?	Can I change money here?	How much is a single room for one night?	Can I have a large cappuccino?	Is there a movie theater near here?
What time do the banks open?	Is this the way to the beach?	Can I have a table in the non-smoking area?	Do you give students a discount?	Can you take me to Disney World?

▶▶ **Activity 2: Designing your new office**

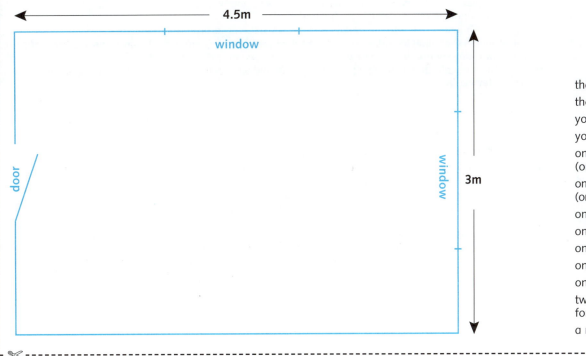

the photocopier
the fax machine
your desk
your partner's desk
one printer (only one!)
one telephone (only one!)
one coffee machine
one wastepaper basket
one poster
one air-conditioning unit
one filing cabinet
two extra chairs for visitors
a refrigerator

▶▶ **Activity 3: What's the best way of …?**

buying a car	making an appointment	learning English	doing research	saying "Happy Birthday"	shopping for clothes
listening to music	planning your vacation	buying an apartment	booking tickets	doing sport	doing your homework
making new friends	organizing your life	playing games	finding a date	finding a job	finding a good school

Communication activities

Teacher's notes

Activity 4

▶▶ **Spot the differences – a communication gap activity**
- Copy and hand out the room outline and items to put in it. Enlarge the room outline if possible.
- Have the students work individually. They can draw larger versions of the room outline if necessary. Each student draws (or writes) small pictures (or labels) of the items in the room, e.g. they draw tennis shoes on the armchair.
- They then work in pairs and discuss where the items are, e.g. *In my room there are tennis shoes on the armchair*. They make a list of the similarities and differences between their two rooms.

Activity 5

▶▶ **Dating agency – a communication gap and discussion activity**
- Copy enough cards for each student to have details of one person.
- Hand out details of one person to each student.
- Have the students complete the details first, with whatever information they wish.
- The students then mingle and try to find a perfect partner. They should ask questions, e.g. *How old are you? What do you do? What kind of sports / music / movies do you like?*
- When the students find a suitable partner, they should sit down. They can explain their reasons to the class afterwards.

Activity 6

▶▶ **Computer trouble – a jigsaw story**
- Make one copy of the picture story for each group of three or four students.
- If you make copies on different color paper, it's easier to keep them separate.
- Cut each copy into twelve cards and mix the cards up.
- Give each group a set of twelve cards and have them work together to put the pictures in the right order.
- When the students have finished, use pictures 6 and 11 to teach the expression *Out of Order* and the verb *to plug something in*.
- Have students act out a conversation in pairs. Student A is the man in the story; Student B is his wife or friend. Student B asks him "How was your day?" and Student A has to tell him what happened. Student B can ask further questions during the story.
- As a follow-up, ask the students to discuss if they've bought a computer. If so, how did they buy it, did they have any problems with it and did they get any help?

Worksheet

▶▶ **Activity 4: Spot the differences**

 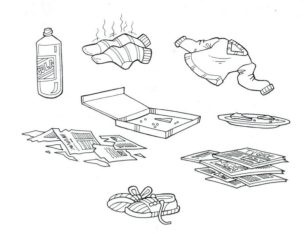

▶▶ **Activity 5: Dating agency**

Name: Amanda Age: 19 Occupation: student / works in a restaurant in the evenings Sports: Movies: romantic Music: Food: vegetarian Going out: Future plans: become a doctor	Name: John Age: 19 Occupation: student / works in a store on weekends Sports: soccer Movies: Music: rock Food: Going out: rock concerts Future Plans: play guitar in a band	Name: Stephanie Age: 21 Occupation: hotel receptionist / doing a teaching course Sports: Movies: comedies Music: Food: vegetarian Going out: Future plans: become a teacher
Name: Anna Age: 22 Occupation: looking for a job Sports: watching football Movies: Music: rock Food: Going out: anywhere cheap Future plans: find a job	Name: Peter Age: 34 Occupation: businessman Sports: Movies: romantic Music: Food: Italian Going out: Future plans: get married and work less	Name: David Age: 25 Occupation: English teacher Sports: swimming Movies: Music: classical Food: Going out: cafes and concerts Future plans: travel around the world

▶▶ **Activity 6: Computer trouble**

Communication activities

Teacher's notes

Activity 7

▶▶ **Find someone who ... – a communication gap activity**
- Copy one chart for each student.
- Distribute the charts and check that the students understand everything.
- Go through the prompts with the students, checking that they know how to make the questions they will need. Some questions are in the present simple, others are in the past simple.
- Demonstrate the game with a student first. Ask *Did you play soccer last weekend?* If the student says *yes*, write his / her name next to the sentence. If he / she says *no*, don't write anything. Whatever the student says, ask one follow-up question – for example, *Did you win?* or *Why not?*
- Then have the student ask you the question for the second sentence – *Do you love watching sport on TV?* Make sure the students understand that they are to write the names only when the person says *yes*, that they can write a name only once, so they have to move around and talk to different students and that they ask a follow-up question each time.
- The students then walk around the class asking questions and writing different names next to the sentences.
- If you don't want to have the students walking around the class, you can ask alternate rows of students to turn around and to ask the students in front of them and to each side of them.
- After a set time of, e.g. ten minutes, ask the students to sit down and report some of their findings to you, e.g. *Jorge didn't play soccer last weekend because he was ill.*

Activity 8

▶▶ **Agreement – a conversation game**
- Copy and cut out one set of eight cards for each student.
- Demonstrate the activity. Ask a student a question with *Can you ...?* or *Do you ...?*
- When the student replies, you use an appropriate card to agree or disagree – and give the student the card. For example:

  Teacher: *Can you ski?*
  Student: *No, I can't.*
  Teacher: *Really? I can. I learned last year in America.*

- Then give the student the *Really? I can.* card.
- Have one or two pairs of students demonstrate.
- Then have the students walk around, talking to different students.
- Tell them the aim of the game is to give away all their cards, so they will have to think of questions that use the present simple and *can*.

Activity 9

▶▶ **Rules and advice – a team game**
- Copy the worksheet enough times for **half** the number of teams in the class.
- Divide the class into teams. You could do the activity as a whole class, i.e. with two teams, or you could have four teams, or perhaps six or eight teams. Each team should have at least four or five students.
- Label the teams A and B and hand out the appropriate list of activities.
- One person from Team A chooses any activity from their list and reads it out. A student from Team B then has to make a sentence about the activity using *have to* or *should*. Ensure that the students use the modal verbs appropriately, i.e. *have to* for obligations (rules) and *should* for advice. Then a student from Team B chooses an activity for Team A, and so on.
- Each team gets two points for each correct sentence. The team with most points at the end is the winner.
- Note: if you have time, the students can repeat an activity but the team answering has to give a different sentence.

Worksheet

▶▶ Activity 7: Find someone who ...

Names

played soccer last weekend

loves watching sport on TV

sometimes travels to watch or play sport

went swimming last week

did some exercise before breakfast

thinks sport is boring

went to the gym today

has more than two pairs of sports shoes

understands American football

plays for a sports team

played tennis last week

sometimes wears a soccer shirt

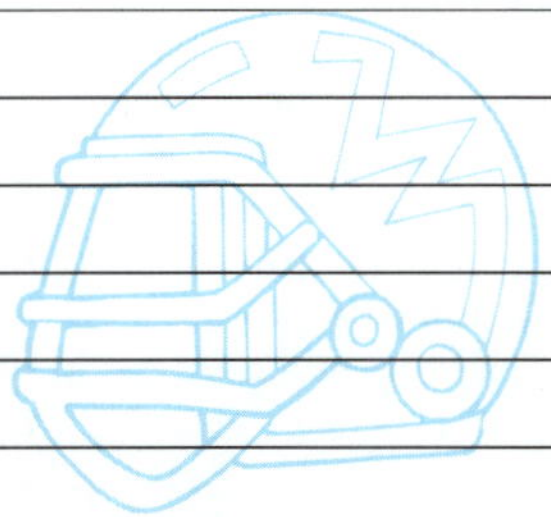

▶▶ Activity 8: Agreement

I can too	I can't either	I don't either	I do too
Really? I can	Really? I can't	Really? I do	Really? I don't
I can too	I can't either	I don't either	I do too
Really? I can	Really? I can't	Really? I do	Really? I don't

▶▶ Activity 9: Rules and advice

Team **A** Choose an activity:

    skiing and snowboarding
    eating healthily
    going to a party
    traveling to another country
    going to a job interview
    managing your money on the Internet
    going to a fancy restaurant
    owning a dog
    buying a car
    meeting a new boyfriend or girlfriend

Team **B** Choose an activity:

    climbing a mountain
    taking an English test
    driving a car
    going to a rock concert
    working out
    writing a long document on a computer
    going to a show at the theater
    renting an apartment
    finding a new job
    opening a bank account

Communication activities

Teacher's notes

Activity 10

▶▶ **The party game – a role-play**
- Make a photocopy of the page and cut up the cards so that each student has one card.
- If you have more than sixteen students, some students can have the same card.
- Demonstrate the activity first with a student: ask the student the question on your card and a follow-up question to get more information.
- Then have a pair of students demonstrate in front of the class. One student asks the other the question on their card and then a follow-up question.
- The other student then does the same with the question on his / her card.
- They then exchange cards and repeat the exercise with different students.
- During the exercise, play background "party music" and encourage the students to imagine they are meeting new people at a party.
- At the end of the activity, the students could discuss the most interesting things they found out during the activity.

Activity 11

▶▶ **Asking for a raise – a role-play**
- This role-play will give the students speaking practice based on the theme of the unit and it will also provide more opportunities to practice the present perfect tense.
- Separate the students into groups of As (teachers) and Bs (principals) so that they can prepare their ideas together.
- Monitor the groups and feed in extra ideas if necessary. For example, the teacher might say that he / she now has a child and needs more money, that he / she has taken another professional qualification, that experience should be rewarded, etc. The principal might say that he / she can't treat this teacher differently from others, that there is a satisfactory pay structure in the school and the teacher will qualify for more money when, e.g. he / she has been there for ten years, that the school already pays well in comparison with others in the area, etc.
- Then put the students into pairs – one teacher and one principal – and have them do the role-play. Listen and note errors for later correction.
- If you wish, the students could repeat the role-play with a different partner.

Activity 12

▶▶ ***Skyline* video quiz – an end-of-course quiz**
- You can play the quiz as a whole class activity or the students could do it in smaller groups.
- You – or one student in each group – read(s) out the questions and give(s) two points for each correct answer.
- If one person (or team) doesn't answer correctly, you can pass the question on to the next person (or team) as a bonus question.
- If you want, you could ask students to write two more questions (individually or in teams).
- It may be a good idea to have a suitable prize to give the winner!

Answers: 1 Luis 2 São Paulo, Brazil 3 Al 4 Hong Kong 5 Jennifer 6 Twice a year 7 Cal thought someone had stolen his car. 8 American football 9 Skiing 10 Because in her country it's normal to arrive at that time 11 Producer 12 Yes, he does

Worksheet

▶▶ **Activity 10: The party game**

What's your favorite kind of party?	What's the worst party you've ever been to?	What clothes did you wear to your last party?	How many people came to your last party?
What time do you usually arrive at and leave parties?	How do you usually go to parties? Do you drive, take a bus or walk?	What kind of food do you like to eat at parties?	Do you like to dance a lot at parties?
Do you like to meet new people at parties or do you prefer to talk to your friends?	What kind of music do you like to hear at parties?	Where is the best place to have a party?	What's the best party you've ever been to?
Have you ever eaten or drunk too much at a party?	How many parties have you been to this year?	Have you ever arrived at the wrong place or the wrong time for a party?	Have you ever been to a Halloween party? What did you wear?

▶▶ **Activity 11: Asking for a raise**

Student **A**

You are a teacher. You are going to ask the principal for a raise. Think of some good reasons why.
How long have you worked for the school?
Have you done any extra work?
Do you have extra responsibilities?
Remember: You don't want to lose your job!

Student **B**

You are the principal of a school. You know that one of your teachers is going to ask for a raise. Think of some good reasons why you can't give more money.
Has the school had any financial problems this year?
Have any other teachers asked for a raise?
What other things do you need to spend money on?
Remember: You don't want the teacher to leave!

▶▶ **Activity 12:** *Skyline* **video quiz**

Do this quiz in pairs. Don't look at your books. How many questions can you get right?

1 Who picked up Mariana at the airport? _____

2 Where is Luis from? _____

3 Who looks after the computers at the agency? _____

4 Where is Jin from? _____

5 Who gets a video from an agency? _____

6 How often are the boys going to clean the bathroom? _____

7 Why did Shawna call the police? _____

8 Which game is the most popular in the United States? _____

9 What do the friends do on their weekend away? _____

10 Why was Mariana late for the party? _____

11 Which job does Shawna want to train for? _____

12 Does Jin think that Shawna will get a raise? _____

Copyright © Macmillan Publishers Limited 2002

PHOTOCOPIABLE

Review Unit for Units 1–6

Teacher's notes

Review Unit for Units 1–6

- Set the scene by telling the students that they are going to watch the second half of a video about the lives of a group of young people living in Boston, a city in the northeast of the U.S.A. They are all working in their first jobs. The video follows the group as their lives change.
- Hand out the worksheets to the students. Ask them to look at the photographs and read the notes about each character. Answer any questions they have.
- Read the summary to the students, and have them complete the worksheet by drawing lines between the characters and writing down the relationship, e.g. *Luis / Sara – boyfriend & girlfriend*. Check the students' answers.
- Ask the students to watch the video and be prepared to tell you who Al is. Let them ask any questions they have.

Summary

Mariana, a creative writer from Venezuela, arrives in Boston. She meets her roommates, Sara and Shawna; and her new neighbors, Luis, Josh and Jin. The boys are roommates. Luis and Sara are boyfriend and girlfriend. At the advertising agency, Mariana meets her new boss, Joan. Joan tells Mariana, Shawna and Luis about their new project, the Fruity Fruit drinks project. They work hard and one night, Shawna misses a date with her boyfriend, Cal, because they have to work late. Mariana also meets Jennifer, Josh's sister. Jennifer shows her a video from a dating agency. Mariana chooses a man, but the date is a disaster. She and Josh begin to like each other.

Video Script   COUNTER 35:29–36:45

In *Skyline* last semester, Mariana came to Boston. She met Luis, Shawna and Sara. And she met Josh and Jin, who live across the hall. Mariana, Shawna and Luis all work together in an advertising agency. They work for Joan. Al works there too. Al does not speak Spanish, but he tries.

Al: Email? Sure, no problem. Oh, I mean no problema no problema.

Mariana: Thanks a lot.

Worksheet

▶▶ **Joan**
Joan owns an advertising agency.

▶▶ **Sara**
Sara is Canadian and plays in a band.

▶▶ **Shawna**
Shawna is an office manager.

boyfriend & girlfriend

▶▶ **Luis**
Luis is Brazilian.

▶▶ **Mariana**
Mariana is from Venezuela.

▶▶ **Cal**
Cal likes football.

▶▶ **Jin**
Jin is a biology major from Hong Kong.

▶▶ **Josh**
Josh is a social work student.

▶▶ **Jennifer**
Jennifer has a bookshop.